PRIMARY-
SECONDARY
PUMPING
MADE
EASY!

Dan Holohan

"The drawings in this book are here to help me put pictures in your head. None of them are to scale, and most of them are missing some hydronic components that you would use when building a system. PLEASE don't use these drawings as blueprints."

Dan Holohan

For the late, great Gil Carlson, who was my teacher

"Whatever goes into a life, must come out of that life."

Whatever goes into a tee must come out of that tee

Alan Levi, Ace Troubleshooter, pointed the beam of his flashlight into the joist bay and settled it right onto those two tees. He turned his head toward me and then said, "How about *that*!" The two tees, one a standard three-quarter by half, the other a Bell & Gossett Monoflo® tee of the same size, were separated by a circle of copper that was about as wide as a gold wedding band. "They're a bit close, don't you think?" Alan said. I nodded and asked him where the branch lines led. "That's the *best* part, Dan," he said. "Follow me."

We climbed the basement stairs, and then another flight of stairs to the second floor of this house that was about as old as I am. We walked down the hallway and into a bath-room that had pink, 1950's tile and an old green-stained bathtub. There was a baseboard convector right next to the tub. Alan pointed at it and smiled. "That's where the pipes go," he said. I shook my head and started to chuckle. "But wait," he said. "It gets even better." He removed the cover, which wasn't hard to do because it was just leaning against the element. Still smiling, he pointed at the boiler drain and the short length of garden hose that some frus-trated heating contractor had installed years before. "How about that *air vent*," Alan said. "Whenever you want some heat, all you have to do is open the boiler drain and spill about ten gallons of 'air' into the bathtub."

"Air?" I said.

"Well you and I would call it water," Alan explained. "But the guy who installed this 'vent' was thinking about air. And that's why my guys are downstairs right now, changing the boiler. The oxygen in the fresh feed water ate the old boiler. I'll bet you didn't know that taking a shower can be dangerous to your boiler."

"I guess the first guy couldn't see which way the water was going." I said.

"Well, he couldn't see it because he didn't rip down the ceiling," Alan replied.

"No, I mean he couldn't 'see it' in his imagination," I added.

The Mind's Eye

When I was growing up in this business, I was lucky enough to sit for a time at the knee of a guy named Gil Carlson. Gil was the man who introduced concepts such as "the point of no pressure change," hydronic flow balance, and primary-secondary pumping, which is what this book is all about. Whenever Gil lectured to engineers he would always beam this big wide grin at the audience and profoundly say in his baritone voice, "Whatever goes *into* a tee, must come *out* of that tee." I'd look at the engineers and laugh at the expressions on their faces. They weren't sure if Gil was kidding. It seemed like such a ridiculously obvious statement – whatever goes *into* a tee, must come *out* of that tee. Everyone in the room would chuckle and Gil would say it again, this time even more profoundly.

It took me years to truly appreciate the simple beauty of Gil's statement and how well it illustrates the fact that ΔP (Delta P, or the difference in pressure between two points) represents the true Zen of hydronic heating. Look to the tee and you will see the beauty of hydronics. Whatever goes into a tee *must* come out of that tee. And *how* it comes out will either make or break your job.

Gil Carlson was one of the first people who helped me to "see" in my mind's eye the magic of the water flowing through the pipes. It was Gil that I thought about when I was on that troubled Monoflo job with Alan Levi. Gil taught me how to visualize and how to distinguish between flow and heat transfer. I learned from him that just because the water is moving doesn't mean the people are going to be comfortable. He showed me how to imagine heat traveling on the flow like a passenger on a train. And he also taught me that the water often decides *not* to move if the pressure differential isn't what it ought to be.

Whatever goes into a tee, *must* come out of that tee.

He passed away on April 28, 1994. He was 72 years old. At the time of his death he held seven U.S. patents and was recognized internationally as one of the foremost authorities on hydronic heating systems.

The late Bob Dilg of Colorado's McNevin Company (B&G's rep in the area) once told me a story about a time when he and Gil worked together at Bell & Gossett's plant in Morton Grove, Illinois. This was during the early 1960s.

"I found Gil standing in the parking lot one day, just after work. He looked bewildered so I asked if he was okay. He said, 'Yes, but someone has stolen my car.' I told him I would go back inside and call the police, but Gil said no, and asked if I would just take him home instead. Doris would be waiting with dinner ready, and she would be worried if he were late. He would call the police from there.

"As we approached his house, I noticed that Gil's car was in the driveway. Gil also spotted the car, and then, without displaying any surprise whatsoever, he said, 'Well, I suppose Doris must have driven me to work today.' That was Gil."

I laughed when Bob told me that story because I once drove Gil from midtown Manhattan to LaGuardia Airport so that he could catch a flight back to Chicago. As he was getting out of the car he turned toward me and asked if he had brought any luggage on this trip. I had to drive all the way back to Manhattan to get it for him.

But it wasn't that he was chronically forgetful; he was just focused on stuff most of us don't see. I think he was watching the magic in his mind, as Einstein must have watched the magic in *his* mind, and when you're doing that, it's easy to forget where you left your car and your luggage.

I was with him in Manhattan once when he reminisced about a problem job he had visited in that same city back in 1953. Hydronic heating was still in its infancy at the time, and so was I. Gil was with Jack Hanley, who was Bell & Gossett's Eastern Field Representative back then, and during their visit to this problem job, Gil managed to come up with the concept of what this book is all about, that being primary-secondary pumping.

It seems that the contractor on that job had used Monoflo tees on some perimeter baseboard loops in this large office building. The problem, however, was that the pressure drop through each Monoflo circuit was too high, and water simply wouldn't move through the radiators. It went into the tees, of course, but it wouldn't come out of the tees in the way that the contractor had hoped it would. It was the same problem that Al Levi and I had looked at in that old house, but on a much grander scale.

After a few calculations, Gil suggested to the contractor that he use small circulators on each branch circuit, and then run the main circulator continuously. That would change the way the water was flowing in and out of the tees, and it should solve the problem once and for all. It sounds simple nowadays, but keep in mind that this was pretty new stuff back in 1953. No one had ever tried this before. The contractor did as Gil suggested and it worked like a charm. And that was how it all began.

Gil graduated from Purdue University as a mechanical engineer and went to work at Bell & Gossett in 1946. He retired from there as their Director of Technical Services in 1988. He also served on the Industry Advisory Committee of Purdue's Herrick Laboratories for 32 years.

In 1953, Gil joined the American Society of Heating and Ventilating Engineers (now ASHRAE). Shortly thereafter, and with B&G's chief engineer, Harold Lockhart, Gil presented the paper, "Compression Tank Selection for Hot Water Heating Systems." At the time, the Lockhart/Carlson paper represented breakthrough thinking in the science of hydronic heating. It greatly simplified the compression tank selection process.

That first paper led to a second – the famous "Point of No Pressure Change" thesis, which proved that hydronic systems operate best when the circulator is pumping away from the compression tank. I borrowed liberally from Gil's thesis when I wrote my book, *Pumping Away*. Nowadays, I sometimes get credited with original thinking because of that book, but the truth is I haven't had an original idea in my life. It was all Gil. And you should also know up front that the engineering in this book also belongs to him. He was the man who figured it all out.

I was just lucky to have been one of his students.

Back in the basement

Alan and I looked at those two closely spaced tees up there in that joist bay and we both knew that just about all the water was flowing along the run instead of through those half-inch branch lines. The distance to and from that baseboard convector in the bathroom was simply too long and those tees were much too close together for this job to work.

When I was first learning about Monoflo tees, I imagined the restriction they present to the water to be like what would happen to traffic on a highway if a tractor-trailer were to jackknife.

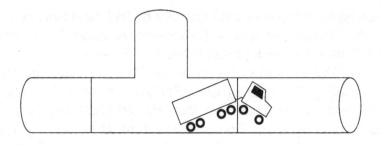

The water in the main is like the traffic on the road. The drivers look up ahead and see the accident so they decide to hop on the service road (the branch circuit) and drive around the accident rather than wait for everyone to merge and squeeze around that tractor trailer that's laying on its side. Does that image work for you as well as it works for me? I sure hope so!

Anyway, here's what a Monoflo tee looks like on the inside.

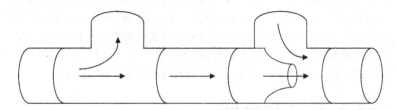

Do you see how the cone inside that tee restricts the flow of water that's trying to make its way along the main? That cone is your "jackknifed tractor-trailer." Some of the water is bound to take the service road. Remember, whatever goes into a tee must come out of that tee.

When Alan and I were on that job I imagined the water entering that first tee (the standard one). The water realized that the jackknifed tractor-trailer was only an inch or so away (inside that second tee), and then it considered its options. It glanced over at the "service road" and realized that if it went that way it would be taking a detour that must have seemed like a 100-mile-long drive. Why the heck should it go all the way up to the second floor, down the hallway, into that baseboard convector in the bathroom, and then work its way all the way back? It made more sense to just be patient, merge, and keep going straight. Seriously, If *you* were the water, isn't that what *you* would do? I know I sure would!

Alan and I again looked up at those two tees. A quarter-inch piece of copper tubing separated them and we knew that very little (if any) water was flowing to that baseboard in the upstairs bathroom. And where there is no flow, there can be no heat.

But here's the challenge that pops up in the real world. When a convector or a radiator doesn't get hot, most folks will try to bleed air from that convector. And even if they don't see any air as they're bleeding they'll just keep bleeding!

On this job, the contractor decided that he couldn't bleed *fast* enough through a normal air vent, and that's why he installed that boiler drain with the short length of garden hose. Now, *that's* what you call an air vent! "You want some heat, ma'am, all you gotta do is just open this valve and dump some water into the tub."

"Okay," she said, "And can I use that same hot water to fill my tub when I want to take a bath?"

"Well, I don't see why not," the contractor decided. "Water is water and it all comes from the same place, right? No sense in wasting!"

I kept thinking about Gil Carlson and what he said about the tees. I imagined myself as the water. I was flowing along the main down there in that basement. I was perfectly happy. The last thing I wanted to do was take that 100-mile-long detour to the bathroom. I'd much rather stay on the highway because I'm basically a lazy guy.

But then that lady decides to take a bath. She opens the hose and starts to drain the system into the bathtub. I'm

7

being tugged toward the tub, and before I know it, I'm flowing right out of that system.

The feed valve opens to replace me with fresh water, which contains lots of oxygen. The oxygen eventually eats the boiler, and that's why Alan's guys were replacing the lady's boiler.

Are you beginning to see the magic?

The key to primary-secondary pumping

I just used the example of a Monoflo system to introduce you to primary-secondary pumping because, within a Monoflo system, we have these two distinct piping circuits that are connected by a bit of common piping.

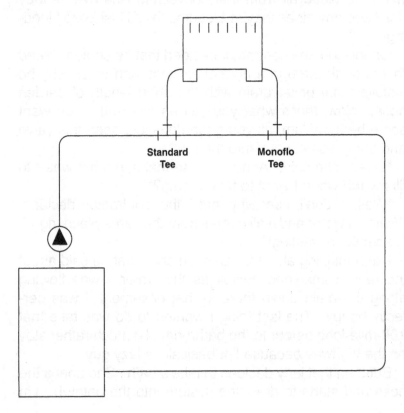

Standard
Tee

Monoflo
Tee

There, see the two circuits? One has the boiler, and the other has the convector. The two circuits meet at the tees. Notice how the piping *between* the tees is common to both circuits. In a Monoflo system you'll have just one circulator, so we can't call this primary-secondary "pumping" but we can certainly call what's going on here primary-secondary "flow."

In my sketch, I've placed the tees so that the distance between them is about the same as the width of the convector. The further apart I move those tees, the more likely it is that water will flow from the boiler's circuit to the convector's circuit. Can you see why? Imagine yourself as the water. The more resistance I add to the main "highway" between the tees, the more attractive that "service road" is going to look to you, right?

Gil Carlson, who wrote mainly to engineers, put it this way. "When two piping circuits are interconnected, flow in one will cause flow in the other, to a degree depending upon the pressure drop in the piping common to both."

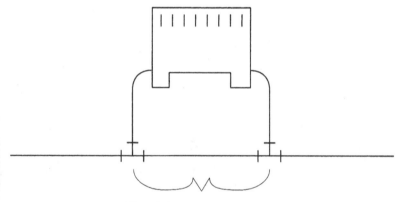

The piping common to both

That business about "the pressure drop in the piping common to both" is the key to understanding primary-secondary pumping. If there is a lot of pressure drop along the run *between* the two tees, more water will flow into the branch. That's why a Monoflo tee has that built-in restriction. The reverse also holds true, of course. Here's how Gil Carlson put it. "When two circuits are interconnected, flow in one will **not** cause flow in the other if the pressure drop in the piping common to both is eliminated."

That's exactly what was wrong with that job Alan and I visited. The pressure drop in the common piping wasn't eliminated, but it sure was reduced by the greater pressure drop the water was seeing on the "service road."

Circuit Piping and Common Piping

Okay, let's make the transition to primary-secondary pumping. How can we eliminate the pressure drop between the primary and the secondary circuits? Simple! All we have to do is pipe the standard tees so that they're very close together. Like this.

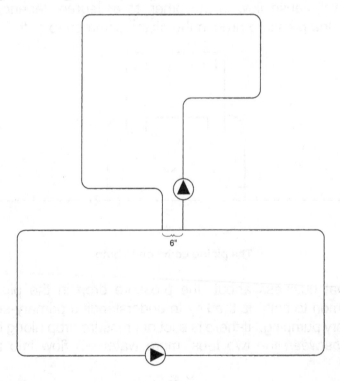

6"

And keep in mind that we're using standard tees here. These are not Monoflo tees. They're just run-of-the-mill copper tees.

Now, just so we can keep things straight, here's what I'd like to do. Let's call any piping that goes to and from a heat source or a heat emitter the "circuit piping." The circuit can be either primary or secondary. We'll call the place where two circuits meet and join "common piping" because both circuits share it. Here, like this.

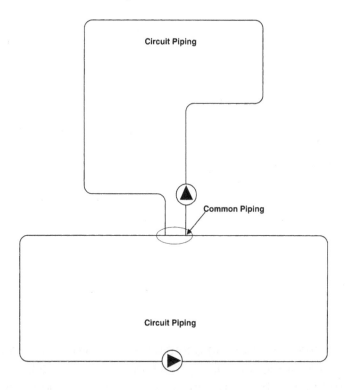

As I said, the common piping gets to be a part of both circuits. As a rule, the shorter the common piping, the better the primary-secondary system will work. Ideally, the common piping shouldn't be more than two feet long (but it can be as short as a close nipple). If you make the common piping longer than two feet the system will still work, but you'll begin to have hot water straying into places where it shouldn't be. Think like water. As those tees get further and further apart, the "service road" starts to look more and more attractive, doesn't it? That's why it's to <u>your</u> benefit to keep the common piping short.

Now let's take a closer look at the circuit piping.

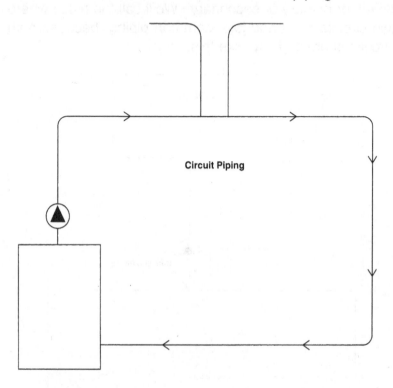

First, the circuit piping contains a circulator. That circulator could serve something that's putting heat into the system (a boiler, a heat exchanger, a solar panel, a heat pump, or whatever). Or it might serve something that's taking heat out of the system (a convector, a radiant panel, an indirect domestic water heater, and so on).

Now, this is one of the neatest things about primary-secondary. Each circulator becomes a "specialist." It has to take care of <u>only</u> the circuit in which it finds itself. This means that even if your system is large, your circulators are probably going to be small. And smaller circulators are less expensive to buy, easier to install, and easier to replace on a cold winter's night. It's the short length of common piping that makes all of this possible. Remember what Gil Carlson said: "When two circuits are interconnected, flow in one will **not** cause flow in the other if the pressure drop in the piping common to both is eliminated."

Or to put it another way, as long as you keep the common piping short, each circulator will run merrily along, without being aware that there are other circulators operating within that system. You can mix and match circulators of different sizes and none of them will affect any of the others. This gives you lots of freedom when you're designing your systems.

Here, let's look at an example.

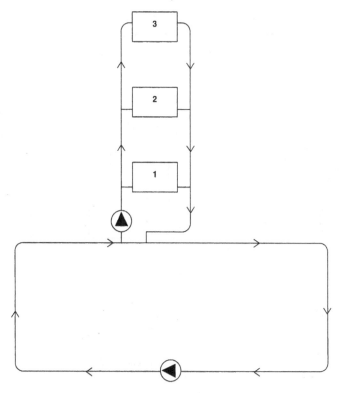

Here we have a primary circulator (the one on the main) and a secondary circulator (the one serving the radiators). The secondary circulator is going to draw hot water from the common piping, just as it would from a boiler. The secondary circulator will pump that hot water through the three radiators that it serves. That's its entire responsibility - to take hot water from the primary circuit (as though it were pulling it from a boiler), send it to the radiators, as needed, and return the cooler water to the primary circuit. It doesn't care about what's going on in other parts of the system. It has its job to do right here and it stays focused on that job. It's concerned only with the flow rate needs of those three radiators, and it sees only the pressure drop of the piping that goes to and from those three radiators. In this way, it's almost like a small residential system, only instead of drawing from a boiler, it's using the common piping as its heat source. A neat way to visualize this would be to imagine a district heating system that's serving all the houses in a small town (they actually do this in many European towns).

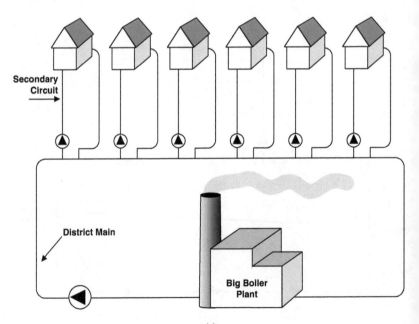

The homes (each with its own piping system) become the secondary circuits. The primary circuit comes and goes from the main boiler plant. The piping inside each house is simple, and the circulators in each house are small because all they have to do is take care of the needs of one little house. This is great because you wind up with lower pressure drops throughout the system. That means that there will be fewer problems with zone valves banging shut because no circulator will be overly powerful. It also means that you can avoid the screaming sounds of high-velocity water flow that often goes hand in hand with oversized circulators.

Okay, now think of it another way. Imagine what it would be like if you had just one BIG circulator at the boiler plant, and it had to move the water through all the houses.

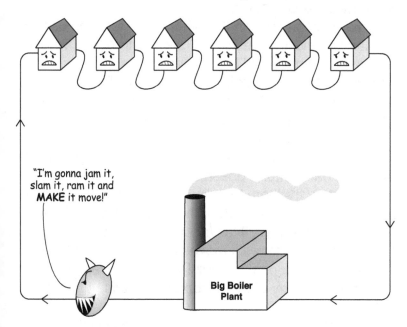

"I'm gonna jam it, slam it, ram it and **MAKE** it move!"

Big Boiler Plant

Pretty scary, isn't it?

With primary-secondary, your systems can be big, but your components stay small, and there's a real advantage to that. Consider a big base-mounted pump. First, you have to provide a concrete base for that Big Boy. You have to anchor and grout that pump in place. You have to use vibration isolators. You have to align the pump and motor shafts with a caliper so that the coupler doesn't grind itself to shrapnel as time goes by. You have to make sure you have the proper approach piping to avoid turbulence at the pump's suction, and you then have to properly support all those big pipes. You have to bring more power to that big pump than you would have to bring to a small pump, and that's probably going to involve some heavy wiring and a big starter panel. And then, if that pump ever breaks down in the middle of the night when the supply house is closed, you'll have to figure out where you're going to get the parts. And when you *do* find those parts they're probably going to be pretty expensive, right?

Primary-secondary, on the other hand, lets you use little circulators, and they're almost always inexpensive inline circulators. What could be better than that?

Okay, it's time to think like water again. The primary circulator's job is to deliver hot water to that common piping. We agree on that, right? And it doesn't matter where the hot water comes from, does it? The primary circulator could be getting it from a boiler, a heat exchanger, a solar panel, a heat pump; it doesn't really make a difference to the circulator. It's there to deliver the goods to the common piping. It's concerned *only* with the flow needs of the primary circuit (which we'll talk about later), and the pressure drop it will encounter as it moves the water around that primary circuit. The primary circulator doesn't feel any pressure drop from any of the secondary circuits. It thinks only of the primary.

Now, watch this. Any flow that takes place in the primary circuit will **not** cause flow to occur in the secondary circuit. How come? Because there is such a limited pressure drop across the common piping!

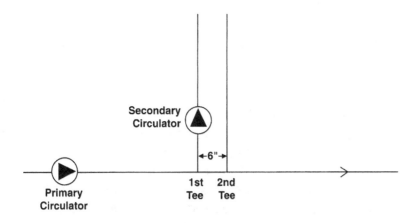

Secondary Circulator

6"

Primary Circulator

1st Tee   2nd Tee

Here, suppose you're the primary circulator. You move water into that first tee. At this point, the secondary circulator is turned off. As you enter that first tee you have a choice to make because whatever enters a tee <u>must</u> leave that tee, right? Okay, let's look at your choices. You can stay on the main highway and travel a total distance of six inches. That will get you past both tees and on your way back to the primary circulator's suction side (which is the point of lowest pressure in this circuit). Or you can flow into, and all the way around, the secondary circuit. It's your choice. Do you move forward six inches? Or do you go over the river and through the woods? And keep in mind, the secondary circulator is off.

What would you do if you were the water?

I know what I'd do.

I'd go straight.

Wouldn't you?

And that's why primary-secondary pumping *works*. The pressure drop along those six inches of common piping is practically nonexistent, so the primary flow stays in the primary circuit until the secondary circulator starts. The two circuits meet and touch for just a brief moment at such a tiny point. And because of this, flow in one circuit won't cause flow in the other circulator.

Make sense?
Good, now watch this.

Two-way streets!

One of the neatest things about primary-secondary pumping is that you can make the water flow backwards across the common piping. It's all in the way you size your circulators. You can also have different temperature drops in different parts of the system, and that's wonderful because it allows you to use smaller circulators. Smaller circulators cost less to buy and they're easier to install. And that's good for you, right?

Let's take a closer look, and as we do, keep in mind that Monoflo system that we talked about earlier.

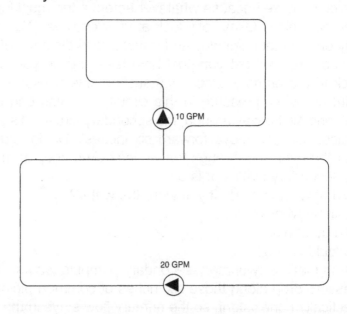

Here we have a primary circuit and a secondary circuit. A short length of common piping connects them. I decided to use a 20 GPM circulator for the primary and a 10 GPM circulator for the secondary. I made that decision after looking at the loads we need in each circuit. Don't concern yourself with the "Why?" of that right now; we'll get to it later, I promise. For now, just watch the way the water moves.

Okay, whatever goes into a tee must come out of a tee, right? So let's say the primary circulator is on and the secondary circulator is off. What's going to happen? Well, let's take a look.

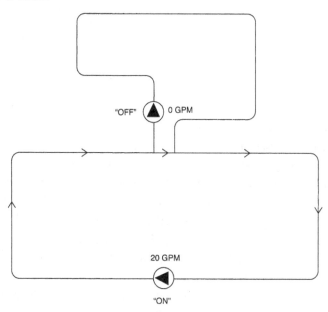

Look at the 20 GPM flowing into the first tee on the common piping. If 20 GPM goes in, then 20 GPM *must* come out. You can't have more and you can't have less. It has to be *exactly* 20 GPM. Now, if you were the water entering that first tee what would you do? Keep in mind that the secondary circulator is off. Are you going to go straight for about six inches? Or are you going to take the "service road" and make that long journey all the way out and back through the secondary circuit?

You're going to go straight, aren't you? Sure you are! This is the same thing that was going on at the house that Al Levi and I visited. Remember?

Okay, let's turn on the secondary circulator.

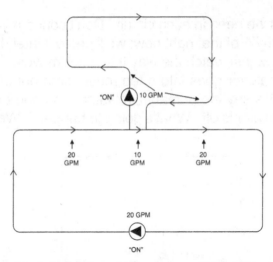

Both circulators are running now. We still have 20 GPM flowing into that first tee on the common piping, but look at how the flow splits in half when the secondary circulator starts. We have 10 GPM flowing up to the secondary circuit, while the other 10 GPM goes straight. Simple, right? It's very similar to what goes on in a Monoflo system that's working as it should, except here we're creating the flow with circulators rather than with fixed restrictions (those jackknifed tractor-trailers).

Let's try something different now. Let's install two circulators with the same flow rate.

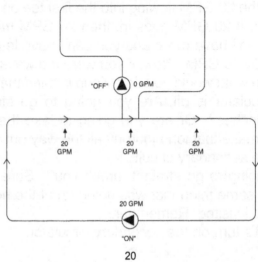

Both circulators can move 20 GPM. When we have the primary circulator running and the secondary circulator off all the water will flow across the common piping and continue on through the primary circuit. Water is lazy and that's why it will always do this.

But watch what happens when both circulators are running.

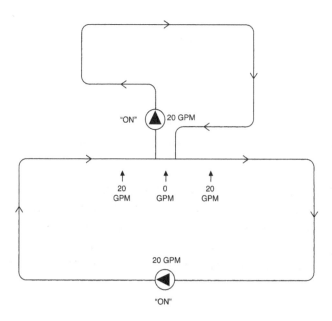

When the secondary circulator starts, it draws all the water out of the first tee and sends it around the secondary circuit. No water flows across the common piping. The entire 20 GPM enters the second tee in the common piping and continues on its way.

Are you following this so far? Great! Let's try it one more way. Let's use the 10 GPM circulator as the primary circulator and the 20 GPM circulator as the secondary circulator. What will happen?

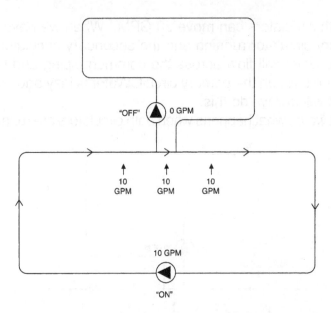

When the primary circulator is on and the secondary circulator is off all the water will flow along the primary. No water moves through the secondary circuit because the length of pipe the two have in common is so short. Now, watch what happens when the secondary circulator starts.

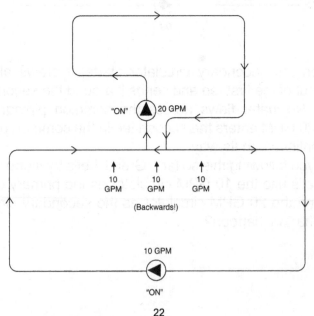

22

To be able to follow this, you have to reverse what Gil Carlson used to say. Let's put it this way: Whatever comes OUT of a tee, must go INTO a tee. It's the same thing said backwards, right? And speaking of backwards, take a close look at the drawing. The secondary circulator is drawing 20 GPM out of the first tee in the common piping. It *has* to do this because we sized it to move 20 GPM. It has no choice but to do this. It's getting that 20 GPM by taking the 10 GPM that's entering the first common tee (from the primary circulator) and another 10 GPM from its own circuit. This portion of the 20 GPM is moving *backwards* across the common piping.

That's the thing about primary-secondary pumping. There are no one-way streets. Whatever goes into a tee must come out of that tee. And whatever comes OUT of a tee must go INTO that tee. In this case, the secondary circulator is drawing 20 GPM out of the primary circuit at the same instant that it's slam-dunking 20 GPM into the primary circuit. And that's how we pull the rabbit out of the hat.

If you're getting stuck on the concept, just be patient with yourself and give it some more thought. Imagine *you're* the water. What would *you* do? It will begin to make sense because none of this stuff is all that complicated. You just have to think like water!

And then there are temperatures to consider

Unless you have leather for skin (or an incredibly accurate water heater), you're going to blend cold water into the hot water when you take a shower. In that last example, we were also blending water so we're bound to wind up with a temperature that is somewhere between the two extremes. We took 10 GPM of water that's already been through the secondary circuit and mixed it with 10 GPM of hot water that was coming straight out of the primary circuit. What we had there was a "mixing valve," even though it looks like a standard tee. That's another neat thing about primary-secondary pumping. Tees get to masquerade as mixing valves.

So why would we want to do this? Well, maybe our secondary circuit doesn't need very hot water. We might be sending water to a radiant panel, for instance. Or the primary circuit might be filled with high-temperature hot water. We might need to raise water from 160°F to 180°F in the secondary circuit. But if there's, say, 350°F water in the primary circuit we're not going to need much of it to get the job done! Some college campuses and government facilities have this sort of high-temperature hot-water system. You can make water a *lot* hotter than 212°F if you keep it bottled up under pressure (about 175-psi in this case).

When those two flows meet inside the tee the resulting temperature that comes out will be cooler than what goes in on the hot side, and hotter than what goes in on the cold side. That's common sense, right? It's the same thing that happens when you take a shower. In this case, the "hot" is what's coming from the primary. The "cold" is the stuff that's recirculating back from the secondary circuit, and the "warm" is what you're sending out to the secondary circuit.

So we need a way to figure out what the "warm" temperature will be. Fortunately, this isn't hard to do. There's a simple math equation that you can use to figure it out. And if you don't like math, don't get nervous. I don't like math either so I've kept things pretty simple in this book. We're going to be using just a few basic equations as we go along and they're not at all difficult to work with.

Here's the first:

(Hot Flow Rate X Hot Temperature) + (Cold Flow Rate X Cold Temperature) = (Warm Flow Rate X Warm Temperature, which we don't yet know)

We call this the Heat Balance equation and it's a very useful tool (as you will see!). And by the way, when we're doing a Heat Balance we can substitute the multiplication symbol (X) for the symbol @, and vice versa. In other words, if we're saying 10 GPM @ 180°F it means the same as if we were saying 10 X 180. Just keep that in mind as we go along.

Okay, let's use that example of the 10-GPM primary circulator and the 20-GPM secondary circulator that we were working with before. Look closely at that supply tee in the common piping. That's the one that has the mixing taking place.

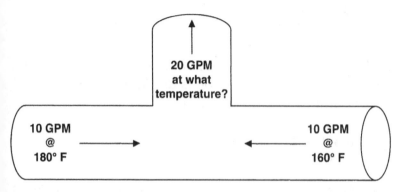

Let's say the primary water temperature is 180 degrees. The stuff that's recirculating from the secondary is 160 degrees. So what happens when we mix the two? To find out, all you have to do is plug in the numbers:

(10 GPM X 180°F) + (10 GPM X 160°F) =
(20 GPM at some temperature we'll call "X")

Now, when you're working an equation like this, you always do the stuff that's inside the parentheses first. In other words, you multiply the flows and the temperatures before adding them together. So, doing the math, we get:

$$(10 \times 180) + (10 \times 160) = 20\ X$$

$$1{,}800 + 1{,}600 = 20X$$

Add those two numbers and we get:

$$3{,}400 = 20\ X$$

Now, in case you don't remember your algebra from High School, to solve for "X" we have to divide both sides of the equation by 20, so let's do that now:

$$\frac{3{,}400}{20} = \frac{20\ X}{20}$$

The two "20s" on the right side of the equation cancel each other so now all we have to do is divide 3,400 by 20 to get the temperature of the warm water.

$$\frac{3{,}400}{20} = 170 \text{ degrees}$$

Which you probably knew instinctively, but keep the Heat Balance equation handy because we'll be using it a *lot* in this book. Not all the numbers we'll look at work out as evenly as these just did!

Another equation!

I mentioned before that by using different temperature drops you get to use smaller circulators. Let me explain this a bit more because it can *really* make a difference.

Let's put you back in the shower for a minute. You're probably using a lot more cold water than hot water to get that perfect mix, right? The cold water that comes in from the street might be 60°F. The hot water, if it's coming from an older boiler that has a tankless coil for making domestic hot water, could be 180°F. Okay, a comfortable shower is going to be about 100°F (any hotter than that and you're doing a jig). The thing to keep in mind is that you don't have to mix in much 180°F water to get that cold water up to 100°F. You know that from experience, right?

Okay, now consider a radiant panel that's operating off a secondary circulator. Suppose we design that panel for 120°F-supply water. On a cold day, the return water that's coming back from the panel is 100°F because that's the way we designed it. We happen to have 180°F water in the primary circuit on this system. Following the same logic, it really shouldn't take much 180°F water to raise the radiant panel's return water temperature from 100°F to 120°F, should it? And if you don't need very much hot supply water then the circulator that's providing that hot water can be relatively small. And the pipe that's supplying the hot water can also be pretty small. In fact (and as you will see), we might not even use a circulator to provide the hot water. We might use a two-way valve instead.

But hold that thought for now. We'll get back to it in a while. First, let's focus on the next equation that we'll be using throughout this book. This one has to do with flow rates and temperature drops. Here 'tis:

$$\frac{BTUH}{\Delta T \times 500} = GPM$$

Let me explain what the parts of the equation mean. Let's get the simple one out of the way first. GPM stands for Gallons Per Minute. It's the standard term that we use in North America when we're talking about hydronic heating systems. We move so many gallons of water per minute and the heat travels on that flow like a passenger on a train. GPM is an expression of volume over time. It has nothing to do with velocity. It's all about the *amount* of water that can move from here to there during one minute.

How *fast* that water moves (the velocity) depends on the size of the pipe through which it's moving, and the circulator that's providing the force. In other words, 10 GPM moves faster in a 1" pipe than it does in a 3" pipe.

Okay, the next component is BTUH. That stands for British Thermal Units per Hour. And in case you don't know (and if you *don't* know, you may be afraid to ask!) a British Thermal Unit is the amount of heat it takes to raise one pound of water (that's about one pint) one degree Fahrenheit. You may sometimes see the term MBH (but not in this formula). That stands for "Thousands of BTUs per Hour." The M in that acronym is the Roman numeral 1,000. I just wanted to mention that because you may not have known, and I know that it's sometimes tough to ask.

The triangle symbol in the equation is the Greek letter Delta. When we're dealing with heating systems, Delta (or Δ) means "Difference in." So Delta T (or ΔT) means "Difference in Temperature." We also use the term Delta P (or ΔP). That means "Difference in Pressure."

When we're talking ΔT we're talking about the difference in temperature between the water that enters a boiler, a convector, a radiant panel, or whatever, and the temperature at which it comes out. Remember that radiant panel we looked at before? The water went in at 120°F and came out at 100°F, right? That's a 20°F ΔT.

Okay, last item in the equation - the number 500. This is actually a shortcut. Since we're using this equation to figure out how much water we have to move in one minute, we have to know something about the water itself. In this case, we need to know that a gallon (as in GALLONS per minute) weighs 8.33 pounds. The other part of the 500 has to do with time (as in gallons per MINUTE). There are, as you well know, 60 minutes in an hour. So if you multiply the weight of a gallon of water (8.33) by 60 minutes you'll come up with 499.8, which we'll round up to 500 to make life a bit easier, and that's where we get that part of the equation.

Pulling it all together, we have a certain amount of heat (from the boiler, or whatever, which is the top part of the equation) and we're using that heat to raise a quantity of water (measured in pounds) a certain amount of degrees Fahrenheit over the course of one minute. Knowing all that, we can figure the flow rate. Make sense?

Okay, here's the next step. And this brings us to **A Great Hydronic Tradition**. If you replace the ΔT symbol with the number 20 (as in a 20°F temperature difference), the bottom part of the equation will now look like this:

20 X 500

Do the multiplication and you'll get the easy-to-remember, simple-to-deal-with number **10,000**. Which brings us to the Rule of Thumb that most of us in this business have used for years:

If you want to know the required heating flow rate, just divide the BTUH load by 10,000.

For instance, if you need to move 100,000 BTUH from a boiler to a bunch of radiators, all you have to do is size a circulator for 10 GPM (100,000 ÷ 10,000 = 10). See how simple life can be? The water goes out into the world and returns 20 degrees cooler.

But when it comes to primary-secondary pumping, if you fall in love with that easy-to-love Rule of Thumb you're probably going to be installing (and paying for) pipes and circulators that are bigger than they need to be.

Here's what I mean. Take a closer look at that 100,000 BTUH load that we have to satisfy. Suppose we figure it on a 40°F temperature drop instead of a 20°F temperature drop. Here's the equation again:

$$\frac{100,000 \text{ BTUH}}{\Delta T \text{ X } 500} = \text{GPM}$$

Substitute 40 for ΔT and look at what happens:

$$\frac{100,000 \text{ BTUH}}{40 \text{ X } 500} = \text{GPM}$$

$$\frac{100,000 \text{ BTUH}}{20,000} = 5 \text{ GPM}$$

See? You just cut the required flow rate in half. You also reduced the size of the pipe you need. You may even reduce the size of the circulator.

Of course, to get the same average water temperature at the radiators (or wherever) you'll have to raise the boiler water temperature. Before, you were sending it out at 180°F and getting it back at 160°F. That gave you an average water temperature of 170°F, which is what really matters to a radiator. To get the same results with the lower flow rate, you'll have to raise the water temperature to 190°F. You'll be returning it at 150°F (190°F - 150°F = 40°F ΔT), but the *average* temperature within the radiators stays at 170°F.

Imagine what you can do if you were able to use, say, 80°F ΔT. Just think about how much smaller your pipes and circulators could be.

$$\frac{100,000 \text{ BTUH}}{\Delta T \text{ X } 500} = \text{GPM}$$

$$\frac{100,000 \text{ BTUH}}{80 \text{ X } 500} = \text{GPM}$$

$$\frac{100,000 \text{ BTUH}}{40,000} = 2.5 \text{ GPM}$$

I'll show you how you can do this with primary-secondary pumping in just a little while, but first...

A few words about Pumping Away

As I mentioned earlier, I wrote a book called *Pumping Away* in 1994. In it, I did my best to explain what Gil Carlson had said during the 1960s about circulators and compression tanks and why, in a closed hydronic system, it was so important to pump away from that tank.

Here's the gist of what I wrote in *Pumping Away*, based on what Gil taught me:

1. A closed hydronic system has just so much water in it.

2. You put air in the compression tank so that when you heat the water and it expands, it will have something to squeeze.

3. The circulator doesn't have to lift the water to the top of the system because the water's already up there. The fill valve saw to that. The circulator in a closed hydronic system is sort of like the motor on a Ferris wheel. It doesn't do any lifting; it just "turns" the water. And as with a Ferris wheel, the weight going up gets balanced by the weight coming down. There's no lifting, just turning.

4. As water flows through the piping, none of it can enter the compression tank because there's just so much water inside the system. If the water left the pipe to go into the compression tank, there would be nothing left in the pipe to take the place of the "missing" water. In other words, you would wind up with outer space inside your pipe, and this, of course, is impossible. So I can tell you with *great* certainty that a circulator in a closed system cannot add water to the compression tank.

5. As the circulator moves water past the compression tank's connection, it can't suck any water out of the tank and put it into the pipes because the pipes are already filled with water, and water is not compressible. In short, you can't put ten pounds in a five-pound bag, so I can also tell you with great certainty that a circulator in a closed system cannot remove a single drop of water from the compression tank.

6. Now, since the circulator can neither add nor remove any water from the compression tank, the circulator cannot affect the pressure *inside* the compression tank, or in the pipe leading to the compression tank. This is because the circulator can't compress or decompress the air that's trapped inside the tank. The only thing that can change the pressure inside the tank is the expansion of the water when the boiler heats it, or the contraction of the water when it cools on the down-cycle.

7. This means that, as far as the circulator is concerned, the compression tank becomes a "point of no pressure change," which is the term Gil Carlson coined.

8. Now, this is the most important part of all. A circulator in a closed system isn't really a "pump." It doesn't actually produce pressure; it produces a *difference* in pressure. That's a very subtle thing that may be hard to see in your mind's eye, but for now, please take my word for it. The important thing is that a circulator can move water by either dropping the pressure on its suction side, or raising the pressure on its discharge side. Either way will work.

9. Since the compression tank is the "point of no pressure change," the circulator will use it as a reference

point. If you pump away from the compression tank, the circulator will show its differential pressure as an *increase* in pressure within the system. If you pump toward the compression tank, the circulator will show its pressure differential as a *decrease* in pressure on the system.

10. And since air dissolves in water in direct proportion to the system pressure, when you increase the system pressure (by pumping away from the compression tank) you will find it very easy to get rid of the air in the system. However, if you insist on putting the circulator on the return side of the system, pumping toward the compression tank, the resulting decrease in overall system pressure will release the air that's dissolved in the water whenever the circulator starts. That will have you down on your knees and bleeding air until it's time for you to retire.

That's the gist of it, and here's a sketch of where a circulator should go in a simple system with just one zone.

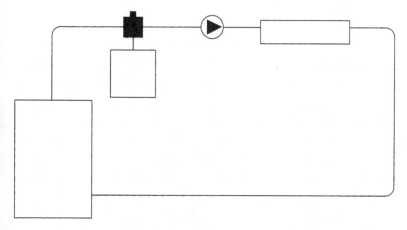

The circulator, in this case, is pumping away from the compression tank. That's easy to see, but let's take a look at how this applies to primary-secondary systems.

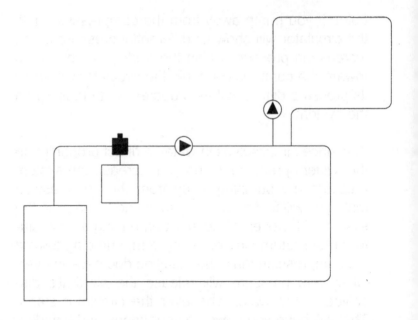

Here, the primary circulator is the one that's moving water through the boiler. As you'll notice, it's pumping away from the compression tank. But take a look at the secondary circulator. It doesn't have a compression tank in its circuit.

Or does it?

This is where you have to think like water. When the water in the secondary circuit gets hot and expands, where will the "extra" water go? If you're thinking that it moves into the primary circuit you're absolutely right! It has to go that way because that's where the compression tank is. And because of this, the secondary circulator will always consider the common piping to be its "point of no pressure change," or to put it another way, its "compression tank."

And that's why, whenever possible, you should pipe your system so that the secondary circulator pumps into the secondary circuit, and away from the common piping. That's a good habit to develop, but there is one case where this might not be the best way to go. Watch.

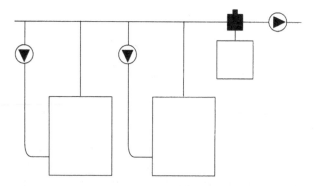

Here, the circulators that are serving the boiler are secondary to the primary circulator (which is the one that's carrying the heated water out to the building). These boilers happen to have a maximum pressure rating of 30 psi. The static fill pressure on this system, however, is 22 psi because the building is four stories tall. We need that much pressure to lift the water to the top of the system and keep it pressurized.

What concerns me in this case is that each boiler circulator will add its differential pressure to the 22 psi that's already inside each boiler. This happens because we're pumping away from the common piping (the "point of no pressure change"). Once the water gets hot, we might be too close to the boiler's relief valve setting when the boiler circulator is running. We don't want that to happen so I'm going to move the circulators to the other side on this job - just to be sure.

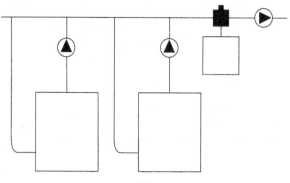

Now that the secondary circulators can't add their differential pressure to the boilers there's no chance that they'll pop the relief valves. The circulators are going to show their pressure differential as a drop in their suction pressure, however.

So why don't I just pipe it this way on every job? Well, because whenever we pump *away* from the compression tank (be it an actual tank or the common piping), the circulator will increase the pressure within the system, and that will help us get rid of trapped air. If we can pump away from the common piping and into a boiler it will help us move air through the boiler. And think about this. Suppose the boiler had a 30-psi rating and the system fill pressure was 12 psi. My secondary circulator (the one on the boiler) probably has a low-head capability anyway because it only has to be concerned with the friction loss through the boiler and the near-boiler piping. With an 18-psi difference between the fill pressure and the relief pressure, I can be pretty sure that my secondary circulator won't pop the relief valve, so I'll pump away from the common piping and into the boiler in that case.

There are more ways than one to get the job done!

We can assign primary-secondary pumping to one of two families. First, there is **one-pipe** primary-secondary. This is what most installers use when they're piping residential and light-commercial systems nowadays. It's also what you see in most of the technical bulletins that equipment manufacturers provide.

Then, there's **two-pipe** primary-secondary, which is what you'll find on BIG jobs (although there's no reason why you couldn't also use two-pipe on a small job).

I'm going to tell you about the two-pipe stuff first because these systems make it a little easier to see what's going on inside the pipes. When it comes to sizing, one-pipe primary-secondary is a bit more complicated than two-pipe primary-secondary because of what goes on with the water temperatures. You'll see what I mean as we move along.

For now, let's start by looking at a typical two-pipe hydronic system. This isn't primary-secondary, but I want to show it to you, just in case you're not familiar with it.

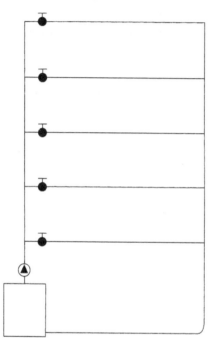

Officially, we call this a two-pipe, direct-return system. "Direct" return means that the first radiator supplied is also the first radiator returned. In other words, the water returns "directly" to the boiler after it leaves the radiator. It doesn't spend any time visiting other parts of the system.

Direct-return systems look like ladders. Trace the flow of water through the piping and ask yourself which way you would go as you enter each tee. And keep in mind that whatever goes into a tee must come out of that tee. When you enter that first tee you're probably going to want to take the shortest route back to the suction side of the circulator, right? I would too. And that's why we have to use balancing valves with this type of system (there's one on the supply side of each branch circuit). The balancing valves are like heating cops. They help direct the traffic (the flow) by making it either easy or difficult for the water to take certain paths through the system. <u>All</u> two-pipe, direct-return systems require balancing.

Here's a two-pipe, reverse-return system.

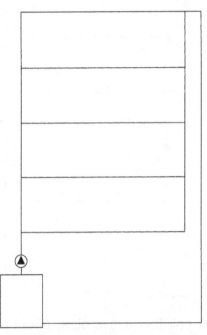

It's the reverse of direct return (hence the name!). The first radiator supplied is the last radiator returned. Trace the path from the boiler to any radiator and then back to the boiler. See how the length of the journey is the same, no matter which way you choose to go? That's the benefit of two-pipe, reverse-return piping. It eliminates the path of least resistance. The flow of water goes into a natural balance, and if the radiators are similar, you don't have to use balancing valves.

The big advantage of a two-pipe system (whether it's direct- or reverse-return) is that the temperature of the water you're delivering to each branch circuit will be about the same (I'm assuming, of course, that you'll be insulating your pipes). This lets you build *very* big heating systems because you can have more or less the same supply temperature at the last radiator that you have at the first.

The challenge with one-pipe systems, on the other hand, is that the supply water gets cooler as it travels from radiator to radiator. Each radiator is removing some of the heat that the next radiator may need. If the system is large, there may not be enough heat left at the end of the run to get the job done. This is what makes one-pipe more difficult to size, but let's put that on the backburner for a while. For now, let's turn the two-pipe, direct-return system into one that also features primary-secondary pumping.

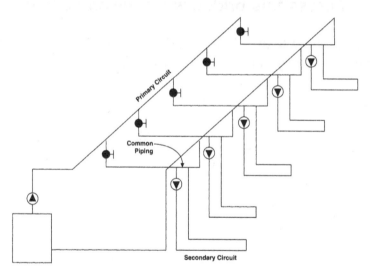

It's very similar, isn't it? We still have the balancing valves to make sure the proper flow is moving through each branch circuit, but instead of having radiators on the branch circuits, we now have common piping that's connecting the primary (the branch circuits) to the secondary circuits. We're making those connections with two standard tees, separated by just six inches of common piping. We're going to supply water to the common piping, just as we would to a radiator. And we'll balance the primary circuit with valves, just as we would if we were sending water to radiators.

Now, here's an important point: The primary circulator will have to be running whenever a secondary circulator is running. That makes sense, doesn't it? If the primary circulator stayed off, the water in the common piping would never get hot. We can cycle the secondary pump on and off if we feel like it, but the primary pump has to be on to deliver the goods to the common piping. It helps to think of the common piping as a "boiler" of sorts. You want to make sure that there's always hot water available at that point.

We'll cross this bridge when we come to it

Okay, now take a look at the piping that crosses over from the supply main to the return main.

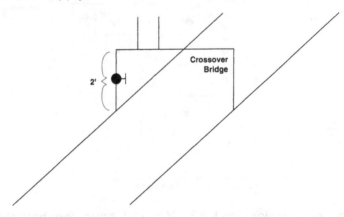

We call this piping the "Crossover Bridge" because that's what it looks like. Hot water crosses over from one side to the other. We balance the flow across the bridge with a balance valve. We might even want to install a device that can indicate flow at this point, so that we'll have a better idea of what's going on. Oh, and I should mention that it doesn't matter how long you make the Crossover Bridge. You can use any length necessary to reach over to where you need to make your secondary-circuit connection. For example, it might not be convenient to have a secondary-circuit pump in a certain location, so you extend your Crossover Bridge to get it to where you can service it more easily as the years go by.

Notice, too, how the Crossover Bridge in our drawing is higher than both the supply and return mains. If you pipe this way, you're giving air an opportunity to work its way up into the secondary circuit where it might get trapped. This can affect the performance of your system because the air separator is in the primary circuit (and usually back in the boiler room). The air that gets trapped in the secondary circuit might not be able to work its way back to the air separator.

You can keep this from happening if you design the system so that the pressure drop across the Crossover Bridge is greater than the bridge's height (in feet) above the supply and return main. Take a look at the drawing and you'll see what I mean. Here, the bridge is two feet higher than the supply and return mains. There's nothing sacred about that number. I just picked it out of the air. The bridge might be 10 feet higher than the supply and return main. Or it might be 15 feet higher, or whatever. So much will depend on the building in which you're working. Just make sure that the pressure difference between the supply and return tees that connect the Crossover Bridge is greater than the bridge's height above the mains. So if the height is two feet (as it is in our example), you'll have to make sure the pressure difference across the bridge is **more** than two feet. On most jobs, this won't be a problem, and with the right pressure differential, you'll have enough flow to keep the air moving across the bridge and it won't get trapped there.

Where you have to be careful on a big job, though, is

when your piping moves further out into the building and away from the primary circulator. Here's what I mean.

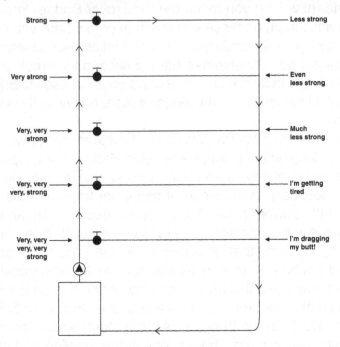

This is that standard two-pipe, direct-return system again. I've labeled it with what I think of as the "power of the pump." It's good to be able to visualize this concept because it's the power of the pump (and the friction loss of the piping) that creates the differential pressures throughout the system. This is what makes the water "come out of the tee" in the way that it does.

You can see that the pump is at its most powerful right at its own discharge flange. That makes sense, doesn't it? And it's at its weakest back at its suction flange (which also makes sense!). Now, look at the way the pump's power diminishes as the water flows through that longest circuit (up to the top and back). This shows you why balancing valves are so important. Look at that difference in strength (or to put it another way, difference in **pressure**) across that first set of tees. On the supply side we have a condition where the pump is VERY, VERY, VERY, VERY STRONG! But on the return side of that same run, the pump is saying, "I'M DRAGGIN MY BUTT!" You can just imagine how quickly water will move across the branch circuit between those two points because of the great difference in pressure. It's like putting air in your car's tires with a 100-psi air compressor. The water (or the air from the compressor) will always take the path of least resistance.

But look at what happens to the difference in pressure (pump strength) as you move further away from the pump's discharge. Up at the top, we're looking at just a slight difference between STRONG and LESS STRONG. And where there is little difference in pressure, there can't be much flow. It's like trying to fill your car's tires to 30 psi when the compressor is set at 31 psi. It's bound to take longer than it would take if you had the compressor set for 100 psi, right?

So when your crossover bridge is a distance from your primary circulator's discharge, and the length of the bridge itself is relatively short, there may not be enough pressure differential across the elevated bridge to keep the air bubbles moving. This is where the balancing valves come in. If you can restrict the flow across those lower "rungs" of your two-pipe "ladder," there will be more water flowing out toward the end of your system, and with more flow, there will be more differential pressure. Got it? Great!

Okay, there's one more thing to consider. When you have an overhead Crossover Bridge you have to be sensitive to the water's velocity. Velocity has a lot to do with the pipe size you've chosen for the Crossover Bridge. If the pipe is too wide, the water will slow down. And when the water starts moving slower than two feet per second, there may not be enough "pull" to yank any air bubbles down the return side of the Crossover Bridge and into the return main. That air will eventually block the water and keep you from delivering the goods to the common piping. And remember, if the water in the common piping is cold, the secondary circuit will also be cold. If you can't get the velocity you need (for whatever reason) install a manual air vent on a tee where the Crossover Bridge turns downward to connect to the return main.

If you balance your systems properly, none of this should be a problem, though. And if possible, pipe the Crossover Bridge **below** the supply and return mains. That way, air will be even less of a nuisance.

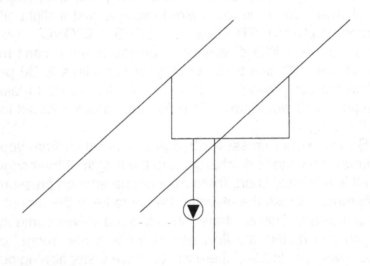

So what size pipe do I need?

Good question! If you're going to have Crossover Bridges you have to know how to size them, so let's go over that now. The first thing you'll have to consider is how much water you'll need to move across the bridge. You'll size the pipe based on that flow rate (which we'll get to in a minute), at a maximum pressure drop of four feet per 100 feet of piping.

Let me first explain what this pressure drop business is all about. You can think of a circulator as a "differential-pressure machine." It moves water by creating points of high and low pressure. And since high-pressure goes to low-pressure (always!) the water has to move the instant the circulator starts. We use the term "total dynamic head" to describe the force that the circulator creates, and we express that force as "feet of head." In a closed system, this has to do with lifting the water because the system is already filled to the brim with water (and pressurized at the top). The weight of the water coming down balances the weight of the water going up. "Feet of head," in this case, has to do with the energy the water loses to friction as it rubs against the insides of the pipes and flows around turns and through the system's components. When I'm talking about sizing the pipe at a maximum pressure drop of four feet per 100 feet of piping, what I mean is that if you want the water to go 100 feet, you have to put in enough energy to make it go 104 feet. That extra four feet represents the energy lost to friction, and that's what we call "pump head."

The "maximum of four feet per 100 feet" is a standard that hydronic designers have used for years. It's the edge of the normally used design range and if you design beyond that point you often wind up with circulators that are bigger than they need to be (and more expensive to buy and to operate).

Here's a chart that will give you a sense of the maximum normally used flow rates in copper tubing of the sizes you might see in a primary-secondary system. These flow rates that I'm showing you will produce four feet of pressure drop for each 100 feet of travel. As you can see, the bigger the pipe is, the more water you can move through it, but in every case, the water is seeing a pressure drop of four feet per 100 feet.

Size	GPM
1/2"	1.5
3/4"	4
1"	8
1-1/4"	14
1-1/2"	22
2"	45
2-1/2"	85
3"	135

Okay, now let's get back to the Crossover Bridge. With two-pipe, primary-secondary, two things can happen with the flow rate across the bridge:

1. The flow rate across the Bridge can be **the same** as the flow rate in the secondary circuit.

2. Or (and this is usually the case) the flow rate across the Bridge can be **less than** the flow rate in the secondary circuit.

We almost *always* see that second possibility in a two-pipe system because the temperature you need in the secondary circuit is cooler than the available temperature of the water in the primary circuit. This is especially true when you're using radiant panels. Here's what I mean.

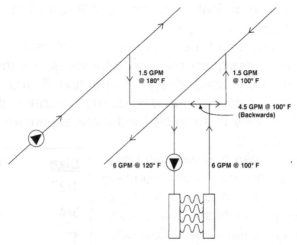

Let's say we've decided to save some money on this job. We're going to blend water across the common piping, without using any sort of mixing valve. Our total radiant load is 60,000 BTUH on the coldest day of the year. We've sized the radiant for a supply temperature of 120°F, and we're expecting to see a 20°F temperature drop (ΔT) on that really cold day. That means that the return temperature of the Crossover Bridge will be 100°F. Take a look at the drawing and you'll see what I mean.

Now, it doesn't take much 180°F water to raise the temperature of 100°F return water to 120°F. And as that little bit of 180°F water flows into the radiant circuit, an equal amount of 100°F return water will leave the radiant circuit and enter the return side of the Crossover Bridge. This has to happen because, in this case, the flow rate within the radiant circuit is going to be greater than the flow rate in the Crossover Bridge. And to make it all work, we're moving 4.5 GPM of 100°F water backwards across the common piping.

Here's the Heat Balance. (You multiply the flow rates by the temperatures. Remember?)

$$\textbf{(1.5 GPM @ 180°F) + (4.5 GPM @ 100°F) =}$$
$$\textbf{6 GPM @ 120°F}$$

Now, let's see how we figured those flow rates. Here's that GPM equation again.

$$\frac{\textbf{BTUH}}{\textbf{ΔT X 500}} \textbf{= GPM}$$

The secondary radiant circuit is working on a 20°F ΔT. In other words, the water is going to enter at 120°F and leave at 100°F. Here's the flow rate we'll need to do that.

$$\frac{\textbf{60,000 BTUH}}{\textbf{20°F ΔT X 500}} \textbf{= 6 GPM}$$

I'd use 1" pipe for that flow rate.

Okay, now consider what's going on within the Crossover Bridge. The water enters at 180°F from the primary supply main, and returns to the primary return main at 100°F. That gives us an 80°F ΔT across the Crossover Bridge. Let's plug that into our equation and see what we get.

$$\frac{60,000 \text{ BTUH}}{80°F \; \Delta T \times 500} = 1.5 \text{ GPM}$$

I'd use 1/2" pipe on that Crossover Bridge. Anything larger than that would be a waste of money. We can get away with this because we don't need that much 180°F water from the primary supply main.

As I said, it's just like what happens when you take a shower. You don't need much 180°F water to raise the cold water to a comfortable level, right? Same thing here. We're just trying to get the 100°F return water from the radiant circuit up to 120°F so that we can send it back out. We need a mere 1.5 GPM of 180°F water to get the job done, and that will fit nicely through a 1/2" pipe. Another plus in sizing it this way is that you get to use smaller balancing valves on your crossover bridges, and that saves you money.

Now, here's something else for you to consider. I just showed you the maximum normally used flow rates for certain size pipe. With that in mind, think about what's going to happen within the common piping when this system is running. We're going to have 4.5 GPM moving backwards across the common piping, and that's where we're doing our temperature mixing. But if we use 1/2" pipe for the common piping the water will be moving too fast, and that concerns me because it can set up what engineers call "jet flow" (along with velocity noise). Jet flow can affect the amount of hot water that enters the secondary circuit and that can lead to complaints from the folks who will be living with this system.

So here's a rule of thumb for you. Whenever you run into a case where the secondary's flow rate is greater than the primary's flow rate **and the common piping is part of a Crossover Bridge:**

1. Size the <u>common piping</u> to be the same size as the secondary piping.

2. Use this larger size pipe for a distance of eight pipe diameters **upstream** of the common piping.

3. And use the larger size pipe for a distance of four pipe diameters **downstream** of the common piping.

That will eliminate the possibility of jet flow and velocity noise. In our example, we'd use 1" pipe in the Crossover Bridge for eight inches before the common piping, and for four inches after the common piping. The common piping itself will also be 1" of course. The rest of the Crossover Bridge can be 1/2". Like this.

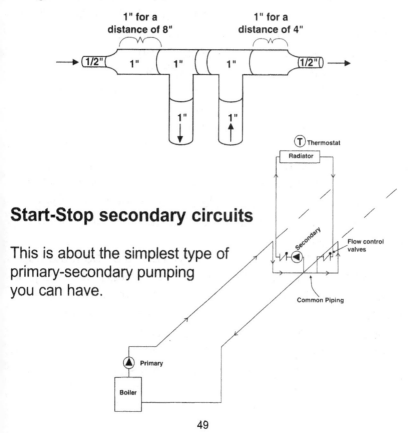

Start-Stop secondary circuits

This is about the simplest type of primary-secondary pumping you can have.

We have a source of heat (the common piping). There's a room thermostat. There's a secondary circulator that starts when the thermostat calls, and stops when the thermostat is satisfied. Naturally, since this is a primary-secondary system, the primary circulator has to be running whenever the secondary circulator starts. The primary "delivers the goods" to the secondary, and without it, we'd just be moving cold water through the secondary circuit. Simple, right?

But, there are a couple of things to consider with this simple set-up. First, be aware that you're liable to have problems with expansion and contraction noises. You've probably heard this noise in homes that have long runs of copper-fin-tube baseboard. These systems have relatively cool water lying in the baseboard when the circulator starts. Suddenly, all that copper gets hit with 180°F water, which causes it to grow. The homeowner hears that tick, tick, ticking sound and wonders what's going on.

You also have to watch the length of your circuits if your secondary circuit is a simple loop system. If there's too much fin-tube on that loop you're liable to run out of heat near the end. A good rule of thumb is to stay under 70 linear feet of 3/4" element in any one loop. That way, your average water temperature won't drop too low near the end of the run. This is especially important if the loop goes from room to room, and the people in the building are going to keep the doors to the rooms closed (as they will with bedrooms and offices).

Notice how I'm using flow-control valves on both the supply and return sides of the secondary circuits? It takes just .6 feet of water head to start lifting the weighted check in the typical flow-control valve. That resistance is generally enough to stop gravity circulation, but you also have to make sure that your tees are close enough together so the pressure drop in the common piping doesn't open the flow-control valves and overheat your secondary circuit.

Also, notice that I'm using two flow-control valves (one

on the supply, the other on the return) because gravity circulation can take place within a single pipe, which means it can come at you from either direction. It works like this.

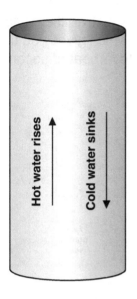

The hot water rises as the cold water sinks. The two flows pass each other within the same pipe. It's another one of those things you have to visualize in your mind's eye.

If you'd rather not use flow-control valves, you can install a thermal leg on both the supply and return piping to the secondary circuit instead. A thermal leg is a U that you form by dropping your secondary piping about two feet below the primary circuit.

The thermal leg can save you some pumping energy because the secondary circulator won't have to lift the weights inside two flow-control valves. I have to say, though, that I've seen a lot of thermal legs pass heated water. They work on some jobs but not on others. I've found that the flow-control valves are usually more reliable.

Whichever way you choose to go, watch the size of your

common piping. Make sure it's large enough to handle the flow rate that will be moving through it. This is especially important for systems where the flow in the secondary circuit is greater than it is in the Crossover Bridge. Remember we talked about that just a little while ago? You want to avoid that "jet flow," which gives you the effect of bypassed flow-control valves (overheated secondary circuits).

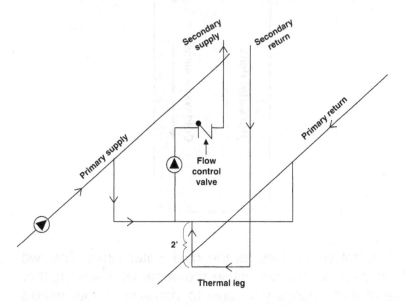

Thermal leg

How to get the most out of a three-way valve

When you're working with two-pipe, primary-secondary systems, there are several ways you can use a three-way valve to lower the water temperature that's heading out to your secondary zone. Some ways are better than others, so let's take a closer look and see if we can figure out what's best for you.

In all cases, the secondary circulator is going to run continuously and you're going to depend on the three-way valve to adjust the temperature of the water to meet the needs of the secondary circuit. This is different from the

Start-Stop method we just looked at. With Start-Stop, we were using a constant temperature and starting and stopping the secondary circulator. To put it another way, we were controlling the zone by manipulating the flow rate, rather than the water temperature. This often leads to ticking noises as a sudden rush of hot water hits the relatively cold pipes within the secondary circuit.

When we add a three-way valve to the secondary circuit, we're controlling the zone by varying the temperature of the water, rather than its flow rate. The change in temperature is usually more gradual here, and that lessens the amount of expansion-and-contraction noise you'll hear coming from the piping. This can also help if you're using PEX tubing in a joist-bay radiant installation. PEX expands a lot more than copper, and by changing the temperature gradually, you can eliminate much of the noise that can take place if you suddenly hit it with hot water.

Okay, here's your first option for piping your 3-way valve in the secondary circuit.

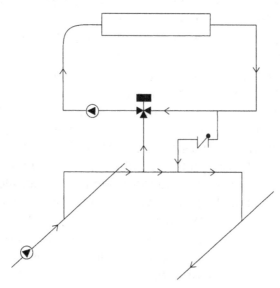

Here, we're using a mixing valve as the three-way valve. Most installers pipe their systems this way. Nowadays, mixing valves are very common, and the manufacturers of radiant heating equipment usually provide them as part of their package. The HOT port of the mixing valve in this drawing is the one on the bottom of the valve. The hot water from the primary circuit enters the valve at that point. The COLD port is the one on the right side of the valve. That's the port that's catching the relatively cold water that's returning from the secondary circuit. We're about to reheat that water and send it out to do some more work. The port at the circulator's suction is the MIXED port. This will provide the proper temperature for the secondary circuit.

It's a common installation, but there are a few disadvantages to piping the three-way valve this way. First, the valve offers a pressure drop right at the circulator's suction. If that pressure drop is high (and you can find this out by looking at the valve manufacturer's literature), the circulator might cavitate as the valve shifts position.

Let me take a minute to explain what cavitation is because it might not be something that you've ever seen first-hand. Cavitation is what happens when you "starve" a circulator for water. The circulator tries to pump out more than it can pull in, and that creates a drastic drop in pressure at the center (the "eye") of the circulator's impeller. This sudden drop in pressure causes the water that's at the eye of the impeller to flash into a vapor. And please understand that when I say "vapor" I'm not talking about steam. This can't be steam because we're not adding additional heat to the water. This is just water in its vapor form. It's the same stuff you get if you put tap water in a cup under a bell jar and then use a vacuum pump to evacuate the air from the bell jar. The water will begin to "boil" at room temperature (because of the low pressure). Maybe you did that in Middle School science. I did, and I clearly recall that my jaw dropped down about this far when the water started to boil in that paper cup.

Now, watch what happens next. Inside the circulator, the centrifugal force that the impeller creates flings the vapor bubbles that are at the eye of the impeller toward the edge of the impeller, where the pressure is higher (because of the centrifugal force). The vapor bubbles suddenly find themselves under higher pressure. And as a result, they instantly collapse. The surrounding water rushes in to fill the void left by those collapsed bubbles and it does this at an alarming rate of speed and with great violence. The water slams into the impeller with a water-hammer force that's strong enough to tear the impeller apart in no time at all. And once that happens, you'll find that there will be much less water flowing around your secondary circuit – and much less heat. And that's not good.

The next drawback to piping your three-way valve as I have it in that drawing is that you're using a flow-control valve on the return riser that's connected back into the Crossover Bridge. The flow-control valve is there to prevent gravity circulation, sure, but look at the direction of flow. See how the water is moving through the flow-control valve and *toward* the Crossover Bridge? Now, think about what's going to happen when the three-way valve is closed to the primary circuit (in other words, when there's no demand for heat in the secondary circuit). At that point, the flow-control valve will act as a check valve, preventing any water in the primary circuit from entering the secondary circuit. As the water temperature in the secondary circuit drops, the water in the secondary circuit will contract because the secondary circuit is now isolated from the system's compression tank. That drop in secondary circuit pressure (due to the water's contraction) might also cause the secondary circulator to cavitate because it won't have the pressure it needs to keep the water at the eye of its impeller in the liquid state. An engineer would say that the circulator lacked N.P.S.H., or **N**et **P**ositive **S**uction **H**ead, which is the available pressure, minus all the pressure drops, leading into a circulator. I was once in a class when Gil Carlson said that N.P.S.H. also stood for "**N**ot **P**umping **S**o **H**ot!" Amen to that.

And with NPSH in mind, this would be a good time to use a thermal leg instead of a flow-control valve in that return line that leads to the Crossover Bridge.

But if you'd like to avoid these potential problems entirely, you can pipe your three-way valve this way instead.

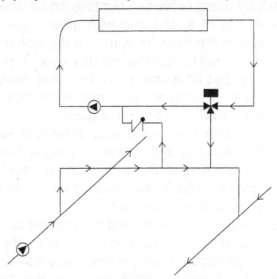

Here, we're using a **diverting valve** as the three-way valve. Diverter valves and mixing valves are not the same and you can't use one in place of the other. Here, take a look inside.

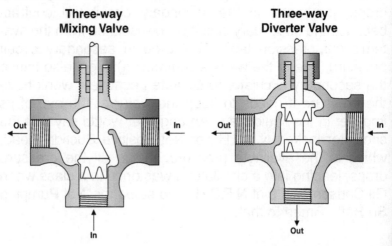

Three-way
Mixing Valve

Three-way
Diverter Valve

Out   In   Out   In

In   Out

See the difference?

- A **mixing valve** has <u>two</u> ways in and <u>one</u> way out.

- A **diverter valve** has <u>one</u> way in and <u>two</u> ways out.

If you try to use a mixing valve as a diverting port you're liable to wind up with a valve that chatters violently and fails long before its time. Ask your supplier of three-way valves to show you their diverting valves because it's definitely to your advantage to know about them. A three-way mixing valve (which is what most radiant heating-equipment manufacturers offer as standard) is **not** a diverter valve.

Okay, back to the drawing. When you pipe the three-way (diverting valve) as I'm showing it here, the circulator will not sense a drop in pressure across the valve on its suction side. When some water diverts out of the secondary circuit and into the primary circuit, an equal amount of water will flow into the secondary circuit through the supply line from the Crossover Bridge. That helps you avoid cavitation. And since the flow-control valve on the supply line from the Crossover Bridge is now facing in the opposite direction, any temperature drop in the secondary circuit will allow the primary circuit's compression tank to push some water into the secondary. That protects the secondary circulator from possible cavitation.

Now, here's something else to consider. You're most likely going to select the three-way valve to be the same size as the pipe in your secondary circuit. For instance, if you're using a 1" line for the secondary, as we did earlier, you'll also be buying a 1" three-way valve. The greater the secondary circuit's flow rate, the bigger (and more expensive) the three-way valve will be.

But keep in mind that the flow rate moving from the primary circuit (on the Crossover Bridge) is usually less than what you'll be seeing in the secondary circuit. That's because of the relatively steep temperature drop you're taking across the Bridge (a full 80°F in the example we looked at before!). Remember that we don't need much hot water to create warm water, and it's the HOT water that's controlling what's going on in the secondary circuit. If we put the three-way valve in the secondary circuit (as we have in the past two examples) we won't be sizing it to the flow rate that's really controlling the temperature (that being the hot water that's entering from the Crossover Bridge). So being line-sized, in this case, also means being **over-sized**, and that can lessen the control you have over the temperature that's flowing around your secondary circuit. Oversized valves tend to "hunt," swinging wildly back and forth across their setpoint.

So I'd like you to consider doing this instead.

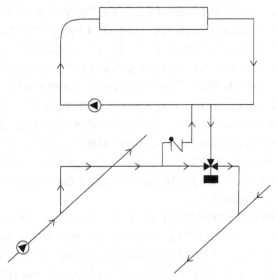

This really gives you the best of all worlds. There's no valve restriction whatsoever on the suction side of the secondary circulator. There's no chance for cavitation from "shrinking" water that's trapped by a flow-control valve and a three-way valve that's in its full-bypass position. And best of all, you just saved money on the three-way mixing valve (notice how it has **two** ways in and **one** way out?) because now, instead of being in the secondary circuit, it's in the smaller Crossover Bridge where the flow rate is less. You also gained more control over the temperature in your secondary circuit because your three-way valve is now sized to the most-important flow, that being the hot water that moves from the primary to the secondary circuit.

Another plus with this method of piping is that you can balance the Crossover Bridge flow rate by selecting the three-way valve based on its Cv rating, which you'll find in the valve manufacturer's product literature. Cv is the number of gallons per minute that will cause a 1-psi drop in pressure across a valve. For example, if the valve's Cv rating is 1 this means that you would have to flow 1 GPM through it before you would see a 1-psi difference in pressure (2.31 feet of head) between the valve's inlet and the valve's outlet. A Cv number always stands for GPM at a 1-psi drop in pressure.

If you try to move more than 1 GPM across that valve, the pressure difference from one side to the other will also change because you can't compress water. Try to see it in your mind's eye. You're moving a volume of water (gallons) during a period of time (one minute). The space available inside the valve isn't going to change, and you can't compress water. So if you want to move that much water during that much time, your only option is to push *harder*. And the harder you push, the more resistance you'll feel pushing back at you.

Here's an example of what I'm talking about. Suppose you wanted to move 2 GPM across that same valve. What would the pressure drop be?

Well, it's easy to figure out because it follows a mathematical rule that states:

Head loss varies as the square of the flow rate.

A "squared" number is any number multiplied by itself. If you wanted to square the number 2, you would do this: 2 X 2 = 4. If you squared the number 4, you would have 4 X 4 = 16, and so on. So if the valve's Cv is 1 that means that 1 GPM causes a 1-psi drop in pressure. If we want to know what's going to happen when we try to shove 2 GPM through that valve, we just have to square the flow rate (2^2 means 2 X 2 = 4) to find out. In this case, the pressure drop would be 4 psi, which is equal to 9.24 feet of head. If we wanted to move 10 GPM through that valve, we would have to have a pump capable of moving 10 GPM at 231 feet of pump head. Can we do it? Yep, but we'd have to buy ourselves a 15-HP, 3500-rpm, base-mounted pump that would be operating at about 20% efficiency. We're probably better off getting ourselves a bigger valve in that case, eh?

It's not a tough concept to grasp, is it? Close your eyes and try to see it in your imagination. The harder you push, the more resistance there will be (as is true of so many things in life). Head loss varies as the square of the flow rate. Think about it until you can *feel* it.

And once you understand this relationship, you can select your three-way valve for a certain pressure drop, at the flow rate you'll need on your Crossover Bridge, and that can go a long way toward helping you balance your system's overall flow rate.

And that brings us to two-way valves

A two-way valve has one way in and one way out. We can use it to shuttle hot water from the primary over to the secondary. Two-way valves can often save you some money on the installation, but there are a few things that you need to watch out for before you decide to use them. Let's take a closer look at how they fit into a primary-secondary system.

Here's a drawing of how some people like to use two-way valves.

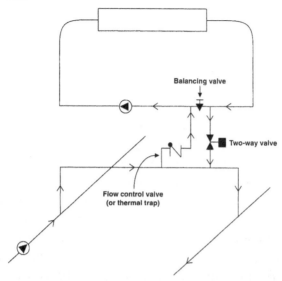

The two-way valve is in the return riser, bleeding relatively cool return water from the secondary circuit back into the primary circuit. An equal amount of hot water bleeds up the supply riser into the secondary circuit.

Now, take a look at that balancing valve. We're always going to need some sort of balancing valve when we're working with two-way valves. And you have to be careful in choosing the valve you use for balancing. You have to be able to throttle it without doing damage to the valve (check with your valve supplier on this). Don't use a gate valve as a balancing valve because, in the throttled position, the gate will shake like mad and the valve stem will wind up leaking.

Here, we have the balancing valve in the secondary circuit's common piping. It's there to resist the flow across the common piping. This will encourage the water to head toward the two-way valve whenever the two-way valve opens. Without the balancing valve, the water in the secondary circuit will just flow around and around because that's its path of least resistance. Little or no water will move between the primary and secondary circuits, even with the two-way valve wide-open. And that's why balancing valves are so important when you're using two-way valves.

This particular two-way valve modulates from a fully closed to a fully open position. By controlling the water that's leaving the secondary circuit, it's indirectly controlling the amount of hot water that's entering the circuit. In that way, it *seems* to be acting like a three-way mixing valve, because it's controlling the *temperature* of the water, as the water's flow rate remains constant.

But the flow rate isn't actually remaining constant, and you have to look closely to see this. When the two-way valve opens and closes, it's not only changing the temperature in the secondary circuit. It's also changing the flow rate. And if you don't set things up properly, this can cause a MAJOR change in the secondary-circuit flow rate. That's why you should consider using a two-way valve only if the amount of hot water you need to bleed into the secondary circuit from the primary is **less than one-third of the secondary-circuit's required flow rate**. For instance, let's say you need to circulate 3 GPM within a radiant secondary circuit. You can use a two-way valve in this case, as long as it doesn't have to move more than 1 GPM to give you the results you're looking for. That's one-third of the required secondary-circuit's flow rate. Get it?

When you're choosing the two-way valve, you should also pay close attention to its pressure drop (which you'll get from its Cv rating). The valve's pressure drop shouldn't be more than 25% of the pressure drop that the secondary circulator is going to see as it moves water around its circuit. So let's say we're flowing 3 GPM @ 4 feet of head within the secondary circuit. The pressure drop of the two-way valve should not be **more than** 1' of head at whatever flow we need to move across the two-way valve because 1' of head is 25% of 4' of head. For instance, let's say we need to move 1 GPM across the valve. We'll want to be sure the valve's pressure drop doesn't exceed 1' at a flow rate of 1 GPM. The Cv of that particular valve would be 1.5. To put it another way, you shouldn't use a valve with a Cv number that is **less than** 1.5, in this case. If the Cv number is higher than 1.5, you'll be in good shape.

Here's why this is so important. Think about how the two-way valve and the balancing valve work together. Without the resistance that the balancing valve offers, no water will move through the two-way valve as it modulates open. That's easy to understand, right?

Okay, now suppose we decide to move a LOT of water through the supply riser to the secondary circuit. And when I say a LOT, I mean as compared to the flow rate of the secondary circuit. For instance, let's say we'd need to circulate 3 GPM around the secondary circuit and we decide, for whatever reason, to move 2 GPM across the two-way valve as we recirculate just 1 GPM. When the two-way valve modulates open, we have to have enough resistance across the balancing valve to make this happen, don't we? Sure we do, and that means that we may have to throttle that balancing valve so that it's almost closed in order to get what we're looking for.

A similar thing happens if we pick a two-way valve that has a high-pressure drop across it (in other words, a low Cv rating). To get water to flow across the two-way valve, we'd *really* have to throttle that balancing valve in the common piping, wouldn't we?

Now, under either of these circumstances, think about what's going to happen once the two-way valve has satisfied the temperature needs of our secondary circuit and closes. All of a sudden, the secondary circulator finds itself up against this MAJOR pressure drop in the common piping, which that nearly closed balancing valve is causing. With all that resistance to flow, the water moving around our secondary circuit is bound to slow, and it might even slow to a point where we have no heat moving toward the radiators (or the radiant panel). And that's going to make *somebody* miserable.

To understand why this happens, we need to look at a pump curve.

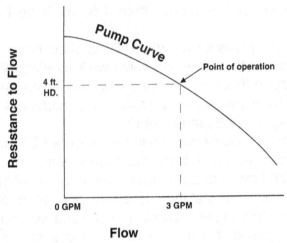

Flow

Pump manufacturers publish these performance curves and they all show the same basic things. Each pump has its unique way of moving water against resistance. The performance curve shows you the relationship between flow and resistance to flow. It's a dance between Gallons Per Minute and resistance (expressed here as Feet of Head). The more resistance there is, the less flow you'll have, and vice versa, of course. On this curve, we have 3 GPM moving against a resistance of 4 feet of head. That's the condition we set up in the example we just looked at. The pump will try to move as much water as it possibly can until the system offers enough resistance to nail the flow rate at a single point. In this case, that point is 3 GPM.

Now, notice how the point of operation on the curve shifts to the left as resistance increases. And as the point shifts to the left, the flow rate slows down.

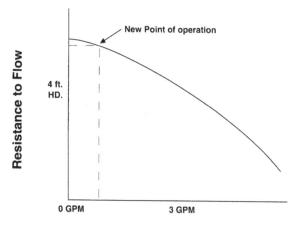

This is what happens when the balancing valve in the secondary circuit's common piping is throttled too much. And keep in mind the reason that it's throttled so much is because either the pressure drop across the two-way valve is high, or we're trying to move too much water from the primary circuit into the secondary circuit. Everything is fine until that two-way valve closes. Then all the water has to make its way across that throttled balancing valve. The resistance to flow builds to a point where hardly any water is moving around the secondary circuit. And where there is no flow, there can be no heat. And again, that's going to make somebody miserable.

The good news is that when we're working with primary-secondary systems that serve low-temperature radiant zones, the amount of hot water we need to move across a two-way valve is usually very low. It's usually less than a third of what the secondary circulator needs to move so you shouldn't run into this problem unless you select a two-way valve that has a high-pressure drop (a low Cv rating). Choose that valve carefully. The cheapest valve may, in the long run, wind up being the most expensive.

But let me show a way around all of these potential problems.

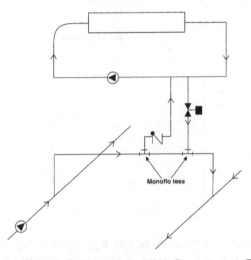

Monoflo tees

Let's put two Monoflo tees in the Crossover Bridge piping instead of using that balancing valve in the common piping of the secondary circuit. The Monoflo tees will send water from the Crossover Bridge to the secondary circuit whenever the two-way valve opens. And when the two-way valve closes, the flow rate in the secondary circuit will remain the same. Only the temperature of the water will change. To balance one Crossover Bridge against the other Crossover Bridges within this system we'll also need balancing valves, but if we take this a step further, there's even a way around that. Watch.

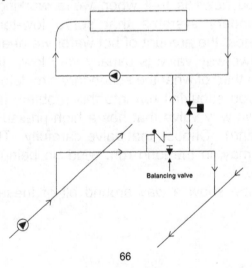

Balancing valve

Instead of the Monoflo tees, let's put the balancing valve in the common piping. That will offer enough resistance to send water from the Crossover Bridge into the secondary circuit when the two-way valve is open. It will also give us a way to balance one Crossover Bridge against the others within the system. If we pipe the balancing valve into the Crossover Bridge's common piping it can't affect the flow rate of the secondary circulator when the two-way valve closes. The pressure drop across the balancing valve (or the Monoflo tees, if you decide to go that way) becomes the responsibility of the primary pump instead of the secondary pump, and that gives us more control over the level of comfort in our secondary circuits.

Another plus of doing it this way is that when you're ready to fill the system for the first time, you can just close the balancing valve in the common piping. That will drive the water through the secondary circuit and the air will come flying out the other end. You'll be able to vent the air back at the boiler through your main purge valve. I'll show you how to do this later.

Injection pumping

Here's yet another option for you (the more options the better, right?). Instead of using a two-way valve and a balancing valve, or a three-way mixing- or diverter valve, let's use a circulator to move the hot water from the primary circuit to the secondary circuit. On the following page is a sketch of what that would look like.

The primary and secondary circulators operate continuously. Each deals with the flow and pressure-drop needs of its own circuit. The injection pump shuttles hot water from the primary to the secondary circuits, as needed.

Now notice how I've put flow-control valves in both the supply and return injection lines. This is a *very* important detail because there's going to be continuous flow in both

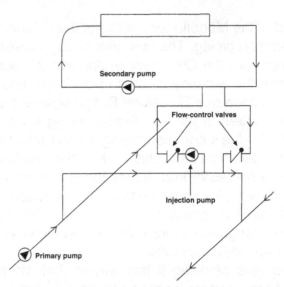

Secondary pump

Flow-control valves

Injection pump

Primary pump

the primary and secondary common piping. That can set up subtle differences in pressure between the four tees that make up the common piping in both the primary and the secondary circuits. This difference in pressure can cause hot water to migrate from the primary to the secondary circuit, which can lead to overheating. The flow-control valves will prevent this. I wouldn't use thermal traps in this case. I like the flow-control valves here because they offer more resistance to flow than a thermal trap does. This isn't a case where we're dealing with gravity circulation (hot water rising as cold water sinks). This is actual flow, caused by slight differences in pressure created by circulators.

Nowadays, primary-secondary injection pumping is all the rage, but it's not at all new. Heating professionals were installing primary-secondary injection systems back in the early-Sixties. The big change, nowadays, is that we have modern electronic controls that can vary the speed of a standard circulator. That lets the injection pump meter the flow of water between the primary and secondary circuits, and this gives us a much greater level of control over the temperature in the secondary circuit.

By contrast, during the early days of hydronic heating,

the start-stop operation of the injection pump would often cause the temperature in the continuously circulated secondary circuit to swing wildly one way and then the other. Those single-speed injection circulators had to run for at least 30 seconds to allow their motors to move from the starting- to the running-winding (short-cycling can kill a circulator's motor). That minimum-run time was a big part of what caused those spikes in temperature in those early systems. This also explains why you don't see many (if any!) older start-stop injection systems. They just didn't work that well back then. Nowadays, though, they work beautifully.

Select the injection pump for the flow rate of the Crossover Bridge. You'll need to give it something to "push" against so make sure you use a throttling valve in the injection line. You're looking for about five feet of head loss across the throttling valve. From there, the variable-speed controller will fine-tune the flow rate. On most radiant heating applications (which is where you'll find most of these injection pumps), a small, water-lubricated circulator is all it takes to get the job done. Oh, and you should use the same size pipe for the injection lines as you do for the Crossover Bridge.

How to size the primary main in a two-pipe, primary-secondary system

As you know, whatever goes into a tee must come out of that tee, and when waters of two different temperatures enter any tee, what comes out will be at a temperature that's somewhere between the two extremes.

And this is what the Heat Balance equation shows us. Remember?

(Hot Flow Rate X Hot Temperature) + (Cold Flow Rate X Cold Temperature) = (Warm Flow Rate X Warm Temperature, which we don't yet know)

When you're ready to size the primary main in a two-pipe, primary-secondary system, you'll do a Heat Balance from Crossover Bridge to Crossover Bridge as they join with the primary return main. You'll see a drop in return water temperature over and over again as the cooler water returns from the Crossover Bridges. It takes a few minutes and a bit of arithmetic to do it right, but it's really worth doing because it's probably going to reduce the size of your primary main and your primary circulator by quite a bit. And that means you'll save money on both the installation and the long-term operating costs of the system.

When you're going through the exercise and you get to the last Crossover Bridge that's returning water to the primary circuit you'll know the lowest temperature that exists in the entire system. Subtract that temperature from the starting temperature (at the boiler) and you'll have the temperature drop (ΔT) across the entire primary main. From there, you just have to plug the numbers into this familiar equation to get your required primary flow rate:

$$\frac{BTUH}{\Delta T \times 500} = GPM$$

Let me show you how doing a bit of math can save you money. As I mentioned earlier, most people in this business like to work with a 20°F ΔT. Now, suppose the total load for this system we want to install is 245,000 BTUH. If we assume a 20°F ΔT we'll wind up with a required flow rate of 24.5 GPM in the primary circuit. That would probably have us installing a 2" copper main, and a relatively large circulator.

But suppose we learn from doing the Heat Balance that we can take a much greater temperature drop across our primary circuit. The greater the temperature drop, the smaller the required flow rate will be, right? And the smaller the flow, the smaller the pipe and pump, and that's certainly to your advantage. I think it's worth doing a little arithmetic, and I'll *prove* it by taking you through an example.

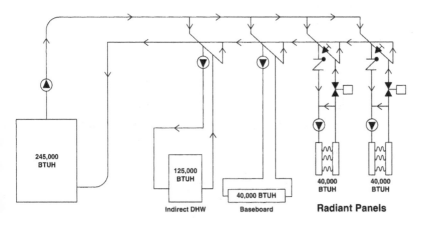

Okay, here we have a system with four secondary circuits. The first is an indirect water heater. Its load is 125,000 BTUH and we're going to supply it with 180°F water from the primary. At full load, the water that returns from the indirect water heater will be 130°F. We know this because we got it right out of the manufacturer's literature.

Next in line, we have some copper fin-tube baseboard convectors. This is on a loop system and we're going to use a secondary circulator that starts and stops. This is the owner's call. We've told him that there will be some expansion and contraction noise when there's a call for heat and he told us that this would not bother him at all. The baseboard load is 40,000 BTUH. We'll supply 180°F water from the primary, and the return temperature going back into the primary circuit will be 160°F on the coldest days of the year.

Finally, we have two radiant circuits that happen to be identical. The load in each is 40,000 BTUH and we've designed it so that it will need 120°F-supply water on the coldest days of the year. We're going to take a 20°F ΔT across each radiant secondary circuit (120°F - 100°F). We'll use two-way valves to make our low-temperature water.

The total load for this job (as you can see by adding up all the secondary-circuit loads) is 245,000 BTUH. Since it's a balanced two-pipe system with a well-insulated primary main, we're able to supply 180°F water to each secondary circuit, without having to be concerned about a drop in water temperature along the way.

Okay, let's take one circuit at a time and see what happens. We'll deal with the indirect water heater first.

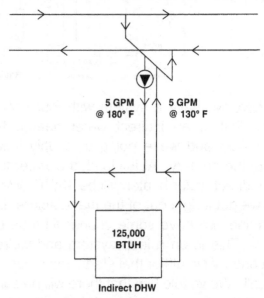

Indirect DHW

The heater manufacturer's literature tells us that, at full draw, this unit needs 5 GPM of 180°F water heating water. They also tell us that the water that enters the heater will take a 50°F drop in temperature, so we know that we'll be returning 5 GPM @ 130°F to the primary circuit.

Now for the baseboard convectors.

We're supplying the baseboard with 4 GPM of 180°F water. On the return side of the Crossover Bridge, we're going to have 4 GPM of 160°F water, and that's what will return to the primary circuit.

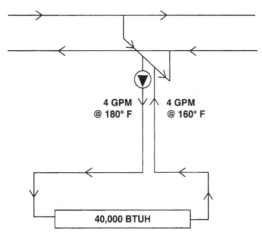

4 GPM @ 180° F   4 GPM @ 160° F

40,000 BTUH

The radiant circuits are identical so we'll just look at one of them.

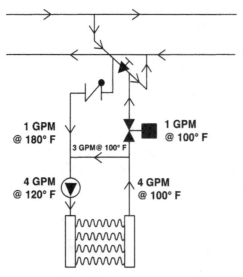

1 GPM @ 180° F   1 GPM @ 100° F

3 GPM @ 100° F

4 GPM @ 120° F   4 GPM @ 100° F

Okay, this one gets a little tricky, but it's nothing that you can't handle. We went over this earlier. The radiant circuit is running on outdoor-air reset control with a two-way valve and a balancing valve that's placed in the common piping of the Crossover Bridge. We know that we're going to be returning 100°F water to the primary circuit because that's the temperature of the water that's returning from the radiant panel when it's real cold outside. But what is the flow rate?

To find out, we just have to use our GPM equation:

$$\frac{BTUH}{\Delta T \times 500} = GPM$$

Plug in the numbers and we get:

$$\frac{40,000}{80°F\ \Delta T \times 500} = GPM$$

Or...

$$\frac{40,000}{40,000} = GPM$$

Or...

$$GPM = 1$$

Simple, right? So we'll be sending 1 GPM of 180°F water into the Crossover Bridge (and we'll use the balancing valve to help us do it). This water will mix with 3 GPM of 100°F that's moving across the common piping in the secondary zone. Like this.

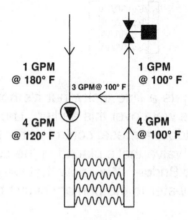

1 GPM
@ 180° F

1 GPM
@ 100° F

3 GPM@ 100° F

4 GPM
@ 120° F

4 GPM
@ 100° F

We can use a two-way valve on this circuit because the water flowing across the two-way valve (1 GPM) isn't more than one-third of the flow (4 GPM) that we need in the radiant circuit. We'll also make sure that the valve we choose doesn't have a high pressure drop.

Here's the Heat Balance that will take place when the recirculated water meets the hot water from the Crossover Bridge:

(3 GPM X 100°F) + (1 GPM X 180°F) = 4 GPM X 120°F

Or...

300 + 180 = 480

Or...

480 = 480

So that balances, and it means that we're going to have 1 GPM of 100°F water flowing from the Crossover Bridge of each secondary radiant circuit into the primary main.

Okay, let's take another look at the whole system, but this time, let's focus on the return side of the primary circuit as these different flows begin to mingle.

First, we have 1 GPM of 100°F water flowing from the secondary radiant circuit at the end of the system. Its flow joins with another 1 GPM of 100°F water that's flowing out of the other radiant circuit's Crossover Bridge. What will happen next is pretty predictable:

(1 GPM @ 100°F) + (1 GPM @ 100°F) = 2 GPM @ 100°F

No big surprise there, right?

Now, this 2 GPM of 100°F water will continue along the primary circuit's return main until it reaches the next Crossover Bridge's return tee. This is the one that's coming from the baseboard convectors, and whatever goes into a tee must come out of that tee, so let's take a look at what's going in. We have:

(2 GPM X 100°F) + (4 GPM X 160°F) = 6 GPM
(at some temperature that's going to be
somewhere between 100°F and 160°F)

Let's do the math:

$$200 + 640 = 6\ X$$

$$840 = 6X$$

$$\frac{840}{6} = \frac{6X}{6}$$

To solve this, we just divide both sides of the equation by the number 6. In this case, X (which is the temperature we're looking for) would be 140°F. So we now have 6 GPM of 140°F water flowing along the primary circuit's return main. It's about to meet up with (and blend with) the water that's returning from the indirect water heater. Let's put those numbers together.

(6 GPM X 140°F) + (5 GPM X 130°F) = 11X

$$840 + 650 = 11X$$

$$1490 = 11X$$

X = 135.45 (which we'll just call 135°F)

So, when we want to know the temperature drop across the primary loop we take 180°F (what we began with) and subtract 135°F (what we ended with).

$$180°F - 135°F = 45°F \; \Delta T$$

We can find the flow rate that we need for the primary circuit by using our GPM equation.

$$\frac{BTUH}{\Delta T \; X \; 500} = GPM$$

Plug in the numbers and we get:

$$\frac{245,000}{45\Delta T \; X \; 500} = GPM$$

Which give us:

$$\frac{245,000}{22,500} = GPM$$

And when we do the division, we get:

GPM = 10.8 (which we'll just call 11 GPM)

Let's pat each other on the back. A few minutes ago, you and I were going to size our primary circuit for 24.5 GPM and we were going to pipe it in 2" copper. We just made a sketch and did an easy math exercise that proves we need only 11 GPM, which means we can now use 1-1/4" copper for our primary circuit. We can also use a smaller circulator. And the best part is we'll get the same results we would get if we had spent more money on the oversized piping and pump.

There is one thing that we have to give thought to, however. We now have 135°F water returning to our boiler. That can cause difficulties for some steel and cast-iron boilers. When the return-water temperature drops below

140°F, there can be a problem with flue-gas condensation inside the boiler. But we can get around this problem by using a system bypass line in the near-boiler piping, and I'll show you how to do that in just a little while. But first, let's try piping it a different way.

Does it matter which secondary circuit comes first?

Let's explore this a bit. Suppose we feed the radiant circuits first, and then the baseboard convector, and finally, the indirect water heater? Do you think that will make a difference in the final water temperature?
Well, there's only one way to find out!

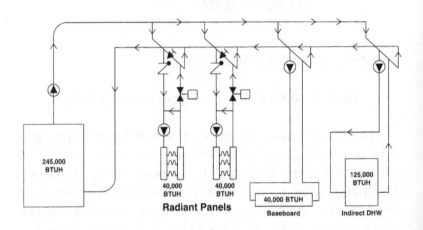

245,000 BTUH

40,000 BTUH   40,000 BTUH
Radiant Panels

40,000 BTUH
Baseboard

125,000 BTUH
Indirect DHW

Let's go through the same exercise, starting with the indirect water heater this time. We have 5 GPM of 130°F water mixing with 4 GPM of 160°F water that's coming back from the baseboard convector. Let's do the math:

(5 GPM X 130°F) + (4 GPM X 160°F) = 9X

650 + 640 + 9X

1290 = 9X

143.3 = X

So we now have 9 GPM of 143.3°F water. It's about to meet 1 GPM of 100°F water. Let's see what happens:

(9 GPM X 143.3°F) + (1 GPM X 100°F) = 10X

1289.7 + 100 = 10X

1389.7 = 10X

138.9 (let's call it 140°F) = X

Now for that last tee. 10 GPM @ 140°F meets 1 GPM @ 100°F. What will we wind up with? Let's run the numbers.

(10 GPM X 140°F) + (1 GPM X 100°F) = 11X

1400 + 100 = 11X

1500 = 11X

136.36°F = X

It's a bit warmer than it was before, but just by a degree or so. And that brings me to another thing that Gil Carlson would often say:

"A difference, to be a difference, has to make a difference."

And it this case, it doesn't, but that can change from job to job, so it pays to check. Now let's try something that's similar, but much more challenging.

One-pipe primary-secondary systems

The main advantage of a two-pipe system is that you can supply the same temperature water to <u>every</u> secondary circuit. That makes life easy because you always know what you're going to get. Nowadays, however, most installers are putting in **one-pipe** primary-secondary systems because these usually cost less to install (there's just one pipe), and at first glance, a one-pipe primary-secondary system seems to be simpler than a two-pipe primary-secondary system.

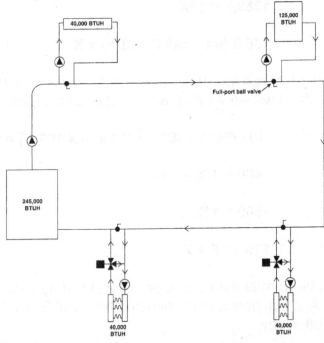

But the challenge we face here is that the water is constantly cooling down as it works its way from secondary circuit to secondary circuit. Or to put it another way, what we just saw happening on the return side of our two-pipe system is happening at the *supply* side in our one-pipe system. And that means that we have to pay very close attention to how we pipe any one-pipe primary-secondary system. Here's a rule that will keep you out of trouble when you're setting up your one-pipe system:

Pipe the circuits that require the <u>hottest</u> water first, starting with the SMALLEST individual load and working your way up to the LARGEST individual load. Then follow the same rule for your low-temperature radiant circuits.

For instance, in the drawing I just showed you we're supplying the baseboard convector circuit first because it calls for 180°F water (just as the indirect water heater does), but the baseboard's load is LESS than the indirect water heater's load, and that's why it's first on line.

So starting with the hottest and the smallest, we do the baseboard first and then we pick up the indirect water heater. From there, we move on to the two radiant circuits. They each need 120°F water, and if we set this up right, we'll have no problem getting that to both of them.

Now, since the water is getting cooler as it moves along, we have to have a way to figure out the supply temperature that's going to be available at each secondary circuit. And we also have to have a way of knowing where to set the boiler's high limit. If we set it at 180°F (as we did earlier in the example of the two-pipe system), there's no way that we can possibly wind up with 180°F water at the indirect water heater. There's going to be a temperature drop in the primary main as soon as that relatively cool water from the baseboard mixes into the primary flow. We have to be concerned about that because we don't want these folks to run out of either heat or hot water on the coldest days of the year. And I know that priority relays are wonderful, but let's first see what we can do with the piping and the pumps.

Okay, let's go over what we know:

1. We know what has to happen within all of the secondary circuits.
2. We also know the size of the boiler (245,000 BTUH).

But here's what we don't know:

1. What flow rate should we have in the primary main?
2. What should be the size of the primary main?
3. What should be the size of the primary circulator?
4. What will be the final temperature at the end of the primary main?
5. At what temperature should we set the high-limit on the boiler?

So how will we figure out all of this? I know that some installers will just take the entire boiler load and base the flow rate and the primary-circuit pipe and pump size on a 20°F ΔT. They'll use the GPM equation:

$$\frac{BTUH}{\Delta T \times 500} = GPM$$

Which would give them:

$$\frac{245,000 \text{ BTUH}}{20°F \ \Delta T \times 500} = 24.5 \text{ GPM}$$

They're assuming a 20°F ΔT across the primary circuit because it makes the math easy. They just divide the boiler load by 10,000 and get 24.5 GPM, which leads them to a 2" primary circuit and a pretty hefty primary pump. They'll also set the boiler's high-limit setting somewhere above 180°F and then hope for the best. If there's a problem, they'll go back and tweak it a bit – and maybe more than once!

But earlier, when we were looking at two-pipe systems, we learned that a little math can save us money, so let's see what we can do with this one-pipe system.

First, let's get past this compulsion to use a 20°F ΔT across the primary circuit. We can design around a *much* deeper temperature drop than that. Our only concern here should be with the temperature that's going to return to the boiler. Let's allow the primary water temperature drop all the way down to 140°F. As you'll see, this will let us reduce the size of the primary circuit, as well as the primary pump. And we'll put a system bypass around the boiler to protect it against low-temperature return water, so that won't be a concern.

But before we can figure the size of the primary main and the primary pump (since we base GPM, in large part, on ΔT), we first have to know the boiler's supply-water temperature. And let's not just guess at it. Let's see if we can back our way into the answer. Okay, we know that we need a minimum of 180°F water at the supply tee that's feeding the indirect heater's secondary circuit. And since we're taking a temperature drop across the previous secondary circuit (the baseboard convectors), we have to start out with a temperature that's hotter than 180°F at the boiler, but by how much?

Here's how we're going to figure it out. Let's pretend, for a moment, that the baseboard isn't there. We had a total load for the system of 245,000 BTUH, and if we remove the load from the baseboard convectors we can get rid of 40,000 BTUH.

245,000 BTUH
- 40,000 BTUH
205,000 BTUH

So that leaves us with a need for 205,000 BTUH at a point in the system where we KNOW we need to have 180°F water. We also decided that we could afford to wind up with 140°F water at the end of the primary main, just before dropping back into the boiler. That means that we can design this system (with the missing baseboard convectors) for a load of 205,000 BTUH at a temperature drop of 40°F, right?

So let's see what flow rate that gives us.

$$\frac{BTUH}{\Delta T \times 500} = GPM$$

Plug in the numbers and this is what we get:

$$\frac{205,000 \ BTUH}{40°F \ \Delta T \times 500} = 10.25 \ GPM$$

Okay, now let's get back to reality. We **know** that we have to take care of that baseboard as well as the indirect water heater and the radiant circuits. So we need to add the baseboard's load back in at this point, and to do that, we're going to use a variation of the GPM equation we've been using all along. Here it is again:

$$\frac{BTUH}{\Delta T \times 500} = GPM$$

In this case, we're going to shift things around a bit, though. We know for certain that we would need 10.25 GPM if the load were 205,000 BTUH and the temperature difference across the system were 40°F. We just figured that out. So let's keep the same flow rate while we change the system load from 205,000 BTUH to the actual 245,000 BTUH. We'll leave the ΔT part of the equation blank and then solve for it. That's going to tell us the high-limit setting for the boiler. Watch:

$$\frac{245,000 \text{ BTUH}}{\Delta T \times 500} = 10.25 \text{ GPM}$$

Now, to solve an equation like this, all you have to do is multiply the GPM by the number 500, in a crisscross sort of way, and then you divide that answer into the BTUH load. Like this:

$$10.25 \times 500 = 5125$$

$$\frac{245,000}{5125} = 47.8°F \ \Delta T$$

Okay, we know for sure that we can end up with 140°F at the end of the primary main. And now we also know that we can afford to take a 47.8°F temperature drop across this system. So let's add the two together and see what we get:

$$\begin{array}{r} 140°F \\ + \ 47.8°F \\ \hline 187.8°F \end{array}$$

That would be the high-limit setting for the boiler. Now, if it's okay with you, I'd like to round that number up to an even 190°F, just to make life simpler. And with that new 50°F temperature difference in mind, let's also fiddle a bit with the flow rate:

$$\frac{245,000 \text{ BTUH}}{50°F \ \Delta T \times 500} = 9.8 \text{ GPM}$$

And 9.8 is close enough to 10 for me to just want to call it 10 GPM, if that's also okay with you. Agreed? Great!

Now, before we move on from here, I'd like you to notice that we just dropped our primary main size from 2" to 1-1/4" and reduced the size of our primary circulator from 24.5 GPM to 10 GPM. Does that make you as happy as it makes me? I thought it would. Use the money you just saved to buy something nice for yourself!

Whatever goes into a tee...

So now we move out toward that first secondary circuit – the one with the baseboard convectors.

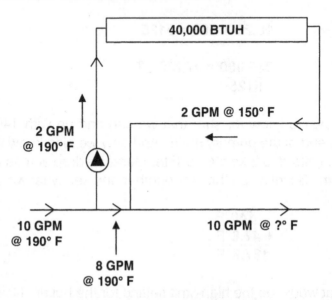

When we were setting up the secondary circuit, we decided to use 180°F water, take a 20°F ΔT across the baseboard, and return with 160°F water. We were going to have 4 GPM flowing within this circuit. This now presents us with a challenge, though, because we have 190°F, and not 180°F, heading toward that circuit. We're going to have to make an adjustment here, but that's easy to do because with baseboard (as with all radiators), we're looking for an **average water temperature**. Originally, we were planning on sending the water in at 180°F and getting it back at 160°F. That had us shooting for an average water temperature of 170°F.

But let's say we send the water in at 190°F (which happens to be our available supply water temperature) and get it back at 150°F instead of 160°F. We'll still have an **average water temperature** of 170°F, so nothing changes as far as the baseboard's output goes. The only difference is that we'll be working with a 40°F ΔT instead of a 20°F ΔT across the circuit, and that means we can change the flow rate in the secondary circuit. Like this:

$$\frac{40,000 \text{ BTUH}}{40°F \text{ ΔT X } 500} = 2 \text{ GPM}$$

So we just cut the required flow rate in half without affecting the output of the baseboard. This isn't going to give us a smaller circulator in this case, though.

Now follow this. At this point, we can say for sure that there will be 10 GPM of 190°F water flowing into that first tee from the primary circuit. We can also say that 2 GPM of 190°F water will head up into the secondary circuit, and that 2 GPM of 150°F will come back through the bull of the return tee on the secondary side. And finally, we can say that 8 GPM of 190°F water will flow straight across the common piping and join with that 2 GPM of 150°F return water. We can say this because whatever goes into a tee must come out of that tee!

Here's a close-up look at that return tee.

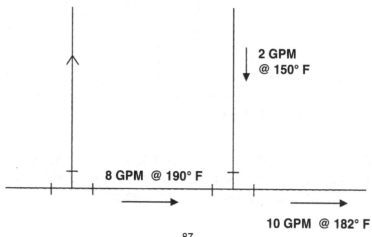

Let's do a Heat Balance on this and see what the new primary temperature will be:

(8 GPM X 190°F) + (2 GPM X 150°F) = (10 GPM at some temperature we'll call "X")

1520 + 300 = 10X

1820 = 10X

X = 182°F

And that's going to be just perfect because our next secondary circuit (the indirect water heater) needs a minimum of 180°F water. We'll be sending 182°F its way so we're in great shape. Let's take a closer look at this next secondary circuit, the one with the indirect water heater.

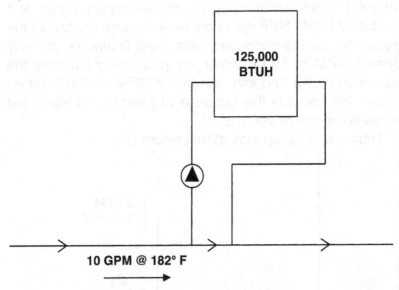

10 GPM @ 182° F

Okay, this brings us once again to a key point. We're *always* going to base the flow rate within the secondary circuit on the temperature drop across that circuit.

Temperature in minus temperature out gives us ∆T, and from there we just have to work the GPM equation. In this case, we know that we're going to have 130°F coming out the return side of the secondary circuit because the manufacturer told us so in their product literature. We were looking to enter the heater at 180°F but we actually have 182°F available so that gives us a 52°F ∆T. Let's find the flow rate by plugging the numbers into the GPM equation:

$$\frac{125{,}000 \text{ BTUH}}{52°F \ \Delta T \ X \ 500} = 4.8 \text{ GPM}$$

Are you following this so far? Okay, if we have 4.8 GPM heading into the secondary and toward the heater that also means that 5.2 GPM of 182°F water will flow straight across the common piping and meet up with 4.8 GPM of 130°F water that's coming out of the heater. Like this:

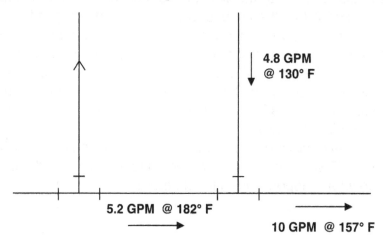

4.8 GPM
@ 130° F

5.2 GPM @ 182° F

10 GPM @ 157° F

Do a Heat Balance on this to learn the new primary-circuit temperature:

(5.2 GPM X 182°F) + (4.8 GPM X 130°F) =

(10 GPM at some temperature we'll call "X")

946.4 + 624 = 10X

1570.4 = 10X

X = 157°F

Easy, isn't it? You'll be sizing your secondary circuits based on the flow rates that will be moving through them, of course. The same goes for your secondary circulators. Keep in mind that primary and secondary circulators have to deal ONLY with the worst-case frictional resistance that they find within the circuits to which they're assigned. And in every case we've looked at so far, the primary circuit's flow rate across the common piping has been greater than the flow rate within the secondary circuit. That means we won't have to enlarge the size of the common piping, or the piping near it to avoid "jet flow" (do you remember that from our earlier discussion?).

So let's move on down the line. We now have 10 GPM of 157°F water heading toward our first radiant circuit. Let's see what happens when it gets there.

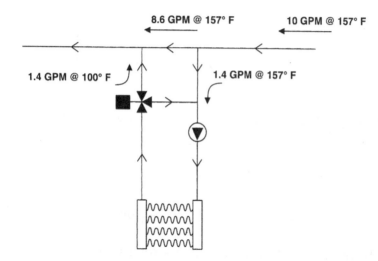

Here, I've decided to use a three-way diverter valve to blend the water within the radiant circuit. I think you'll see why once we figure out what's going on with the flow rates.

We have 10 GPM of 157°F water entering the first tee. How much water will flow toward the radiant circuit? Well, that's easy to figure out. We just have to take the difference between the supply temperature (157°F) and the water that's coming back from the radiant circuit, which, we learned from our radiant design, is 100°F on the coldest days of the year. That gives us a 57°F ΔT. And since we know the radiant load is 40,000 BTUH (again, from our radiant design), we can plug the numbers into the GPM equation:

$$\frac{40,000 \text{ BTUH}}{57°F \text{ } \Delta T \text{ X } 500} = 1.4 \text{ GPM}$$

And that's why I chose the three-way diverter valve rather than the two-way valve for mixing the radiant-circuit water, in this case. That flow rate of 1.4 GPM is more than one-third (33%) of the flow rate that's moving around the radiant circuit. If we used a two-way valve I think we'd have to throttle the balancing valve too much, and that could give us flow problems in the radiant circuit. We talked about this earlier. Remember?

And if you're not sure how to figure the percentage of flow, it goes like this:

$$\frac{\textbf{GPM heading into the secondary zone}}{\textbf{GPM flowing around the secondary zone}} \textbf{X 100 = \% of flow}$$

Here are the actual numbers:

$$\frac{1.4}{4} = 3.5 \text{ X } 100 = 35\% \text{ (too much!)}$$

So here's what's going on in the return tee:

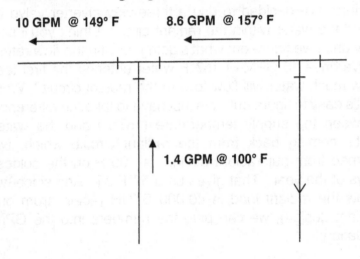

10 GPM @ 149° F   **8.6 GPM @ 157° F**

1.4 GPM @ 100° F

And here's the Heat Balance for this one:

$$\textbf{(8.6 GPM X 157°F) + (1.4 GPM X 100°F)}$$
$$\textbf{= 10 GPM @ 149°F}$$

So, we'll have 149°F water heading toward the last radiant circuit. Now before we leave here, let's take a look at what's going on <u>within</u> the radiant circuit.

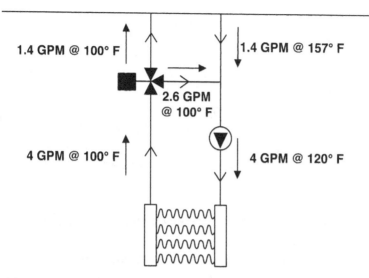

1.4 GPM @ 100° F

1.4 GPM @ 157° F

2.6 GPM @ 100° F

4 GPM @ 100° F

4 GPM @ 120° F

Here's how we're getting that 120°F-supply water for the radiant circuit. We're bringing in 1.4 GPM of 157°F from the primary, and that means that we're also sending 1.4 GPM of 100°F water back to the primary. If there's 4 GPM flowing around the radiant circuit, then 2.6 GPM of 100°F water has to be moving across the common piping within the radiant circuit. Let's do a Heat Balance on those two flows:

(2.6 GPM X 100°F) + (1.4 GPM X 157°F)
= 4 GPM of 120°F

It all balances! Now, the last radiant circuit happens to be identical to the first, so the only thing we need to change is the temperature of the water that's moving across the common piping, which we now know, is 149°F. Let's do our final Heat Balance:

(8.6 GPM X 149°F) + (1.4 GPM X 100°F)
= 10 GPM @ 142°F

And there you have it! We'll get water at about 142°F returning to our boiler. We had planned on 140°F, but we rounded-off some numbers along the way and that's why we're seeing a slight difference now. And there's no need to be concerned about flue-gas condensation within the boiler because this is the <u>worst</u> case we're looking at here, and we're still above 140°F. As a further precaution, though, we'll also put a system bypass around the boiler. I'll show you how to do that in a little while, but first, let's take a look at another way that you can do a one-pipe system. This way is very popular nowadays. It involves using manifolds.

One-pipe systems with secondary manifolds

Here's a simplified drawing of how we'd use secondary manifolds on the system we've been working with.

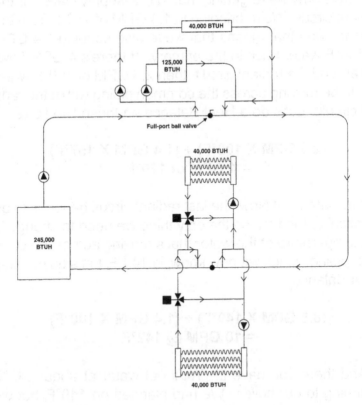

We're keeping the hot stuff on one manifold and the cooler stuff on the other, and we're feeding the hot manifold first. Within the secondary-circuit's manifold, I'm dealing with the larger flow rate first so that if I wanted to, I could reduce the size of the manifold as I shed load. In this case, there are only two zones so I would use 1" for both the supply and return manifolds, and I'd also pipe 1" off the primary.

The first thing that manifolds do for us is to simplify the required-temperature situation. Here, we can provide 180°F water to both the baseboard and indirect water heater at the same time. It's a little like a two-pipe system in this regard. If you remember from our last example, we had to pretend the baseboard circuit wasn't there, and then we had to back our way into the required high-limit temperature at the boiler. That was because the 180°F water cooled as it mixed with the return from the baseboard convectors. There was no way that we could start with 180°F at the boiler and get it to *both* secondary circuits, but with manifolds, we can do that easily. And that's great because now we can run the boiler 10°F cooler than we needed to run it before, which means we'll have less standby loss. Of course, we'll have to adjust the flow rate in the primary because of this, so let's do that now and get it out of the way.

We start by looking at the allowable temperature drop across the primary circuit. We're beginning with 180°F and we know we can end with 140°F, the minimum temperature that most cast-iron and steel boilers can handle. So that gives us a 40°F ΔT. Let's find the GPM we'll need for the primary circulator:

$$\frac{245,000 \text{ BTUH}}{40°F \text{ } \Delta T \text{ X } 500} = 12 \text{ GPM}$$

A 1-1/4" main can handle up to 14 GPM. We have 12 GPM, so the primary circuit's pipe size hasn't changed from our last example. What does change with manifolds, though, is that we now have more places where flows of different temperatures can mingle and blend. Let's take a look at some of the possibilities.

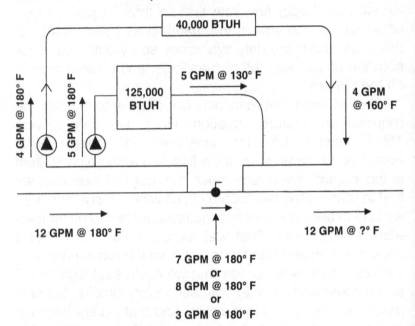

See? Not only are the waters blending on the return side of the common piping, they're also mixing within the return manifold. Let's try starting the circuits one at a time. Then we'll watch what happens as the circuits operate together. We'll begin with the indirect water heater. Here it is all by itself.

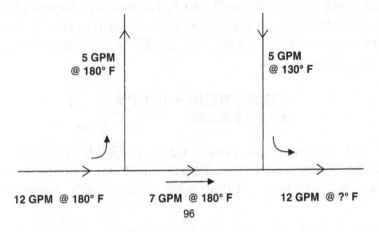

Whatever goes into a tee must come out of that tee, right? In this case 12 GPM of 180°F enters the first tee. The secondary circulator draws off 5 GPM of 180°F water, which leaves 7 GPM at the same temperature to flow across the common piping and meets up with the 5 GPM of 130°F return water. Let's do a Heat Balance on that combined flow:

(7 GPM X 180°F) + (5 GPM X 130°F) = 12 GPM @ 159°F

And that's what will head toward the radiant circuits' supply manifold. We need only 120°F there, so we're doing okay so far. Now, let's see what it looks like with just the baseboard zone running.

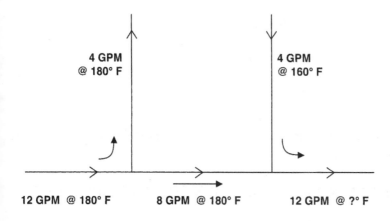

4 GPM @ 180° F		4 GPM @ 160° F
12 GPM @ 180° F	8 GPM @ 180° F	12 GPM @ ?° F

Here's the Heat Balance for the baseboard when it's running by itself:

(8 GPM X 180°F) + (4 GPM X 160°F) = 12 GPM @ 173°F

No problem here either! But what happens when both the indirect water heater and the baseboard zones are running at the same time? We're going to have **two** places where the waters are mixing, right? There's mixing going on in the return manifold, as well as in the return side of the common piping. That complicates things a bit, but it's not hard to figure out if we take it one step at a time. Here's what it looks like.

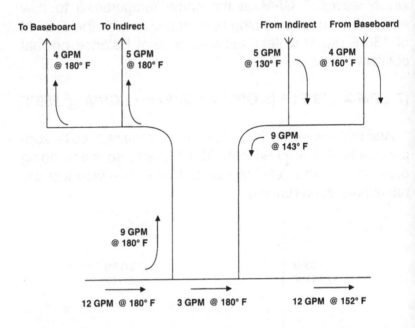

Ready for another Heat Balance? Here's what's going on in the manifold:

(5 GPM X 130°F) + (4 GPM X 160°F) = 9 GPM @ 143°F

And that 143°F will now flow into the common piping and meet up with 3 GPM of 180°F that moved across the common piping from the supply side.

Are you following these flow rates? If 12 GPM entered the common piping on the supply side, and 9 GPM (5 + 4) headed toward the indirect heater and the baseboard, then 3 GPM has to flow across the common piping because whatever enters...well, you know why!

Now for the Heat Balance on that all-important mix back in the primary main:

(9 GPM X 143°F) + (3 GPM X 180°F) = 12 GPM @ 152°F

And since 152°F is still hotter than 120°F, our radiant zones should be in pretty good shape. So let's move over there and see what will happen next.

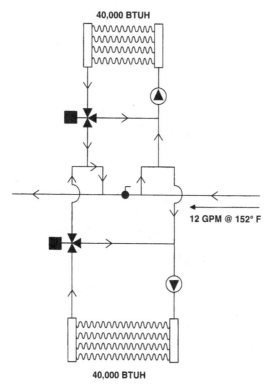

First, we have to figure the flow rate we'll need for each radiant circuit. We know that under the worst circumstances (with the indirect heater and the baseboard both operating) the minimum supply temperature will be 152°F. We also know that the return temperature from the radiant circuits will be 100°F. That gives us a 52°F ΔT, so let's find the required flow rate for each radiant circuit.

$$\frac{40,000 \text{ BTUH}}{52°F \text{ } \Delta T \text{ X } 500} = 1.5 \text{ GPM}$$

And since 1.5 is more than 33% of the 4 GPM that will be circulating within the radiant circuits, we're going to use three-way diverter valves instead of two-way valves, as we did earlier.

Okay, let's see what happens under the worst-case situation when just one radiant zone comes on.

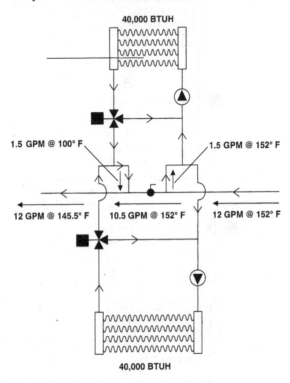

If 12 GPM of 152°F water enters the first tee, and 1.5 GPM heads toward the radiant zone that's calling for heat, then 10.5 GPM of 152°F will move across the common piping and meet up with 1.5 GPM of 100°F on the other side. So on to the Heat Balance:

$$\textbf{(10.5 GPM X 152°F) + (1.5 GPM X 100°F)}$$
$$\textbf{= 12 GPM @ 145.5°F}$$

And that's what will return to the boiler. But what happens when *everything* is running? Let's turn on that second radiant zone and find out.

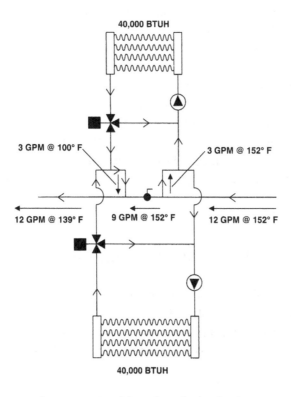

40,000 BTUH

3 GPM @ 100° F.

3 GPM @ 152° F

12 GPM @ 139° F   9 GPM @ 152° F   12 GPM @ 152° F

40,000 BTUH

Again, we have water blending in both the return manifold and the common piping. We don't have to go through a Heat Balance for what's happening in the return manifold because we have two identical flows (1.5 GPM each) meeting at the same temperature (100°F). We'll wind up with 3 GPM of 100°F flowing into the common piping, and it will meet 9 GPM of 152°F water. Here's what will happen:

(3 GPM X 100°F) + (9 GPM X 152°F) = 12 GPM @ 139°F

So we'll have 139°F water returning to the boiler. That's close enough to the minimum of 140°F to keep me comfortable, especially considering that this is the worst case scenario, and we rounded-off numbers to get here. And keep in mind that we'll also have that boiler-bypass line to protect the boiler from flue-gas condensation, so there's no cause for concern.

So, do manifolds make sense? You bet they do! Especially when the entire primary circuit is in the boiler room. If you're using the primary circuit to reach out into a building and act as a distribution point for lots of remote secondary circuits, then it probably makes more sense to go the other way and use individual secondary circuits rather than manifolds. Whichever way you decide to go, you now know how to figure all the pipes, pumps, and temperatures.

And isn't that a great feeling?

What you should know about four-way valves

Four-way valves and radiant heating systems go hand in hand. This valve's job is to temper the water that's heading out to the radiant circuit, and to raise the temperature of the return water before it enters the boiler. Here's how it fits into the system.

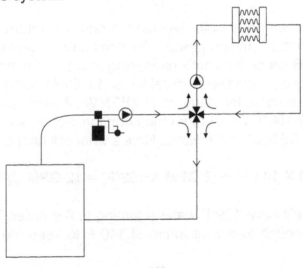

Notice the primary and the secondary circulators. The primary is moving hot boiler water in two directions. It's raising the temperature of the water that's heading toward the radiant circuit, and it's also raising the temperature of the return water before it has a chance to hit the boiler. The secondary circulator is also taking water from two directions – the boiler and the radiant return. It all works because of the pressure differential across the four ports of the valve. The valve is actually the common piping in this case. Here's what it looks like on the inside.

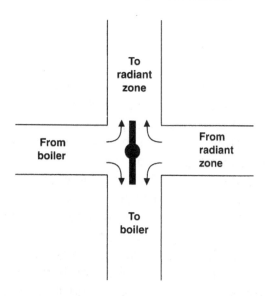

It's just a simple paddle that moves back and forth, changing the pressure drop relationship between the four ports. Four-way valves often have modulating motors that adjust the radiant supply water temperature based on the outdoor air temperature. The motor isn't necessary, but it does make temperature control a lot easier, and very automatic.

From time to time, however, you may run into a drawing that shows a four-way valve with just one circulator. It will look like this.

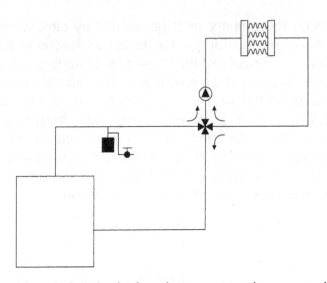

Now, this obviously isn't primary-secondary pumping because we have only one pump, but some manufacturers (particularly the European equipment manufacturers) use this drawing. They can save the expense of the primary pump because some European boilers are less sensitive to flue-gas condensation than some American-made boilers. This is a function of design because there are laws in many European countries that limit the maximum design temperature that heating professionals are allowed to use. That means that these folks see lower return temperatures as a matter of course. Their boilers are often better able to deal with low-temperature return water, and that accounts for the single circulator.

Here, if you take a close look at the sketch, you'll see that, when you have just one circulator, little if any boiler water will blend into the water that's returning from the radiant circuit. This is because of "The power of the pump." Remember earlier when we were talking about how a pump is very, very, very, very strong at its discharge, but then that pressure quickly drops as the water flows around the system and loses its energy to friction? Well, that also applies here. Let's give this single pump some power. We'll say that it can produce a

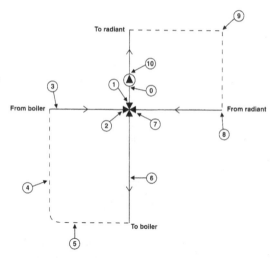

make-believe power of "10" at its discharge. This power, of course, will drop to zero at its suction. Watch what happens.

Now, follow the water as it flows from the pump's discharge. It heads off toward the radiant circuit, losing energy along the way. When the flow returns to the port on the right-hand side of the four-way valve, it has already dropped from "10" to a power of "7" and now it has to make a choice. Should it flow directly back to the suction side of the circulator where the pressure is "0," or should it flow through the boiler? Well, depending on the position of the four-way valve's paddle, the water can (and will!) go either way. In this case, let's say the valve is throttled in such a way that water flows both to the pump's suction and through the boiler.

Okay, watch what happens as the water continues on its way through the boiler. The pressure keeps dropping until the water reaches the port on the left-hand side of the four-way valve. At this point, the pressure has diminished to a power of "2." From there, all of it flows back to the pump's suction. Nothing heads from the boiler to the lower tapping on the four-way valve.

It's easy to see why this happens. Just imagine yourself as water and remember that whatever goes into a tee must come out of that tee. A four-way valve is nothing more than a tee, so take a closer look.

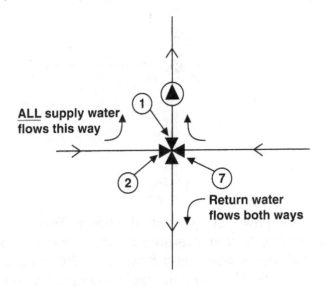

ALL supply water flows this way

Return water flows both ways

The power entering the right-hand side of the four-way valve is "7" while the power at the left-hand side is a mere "2." This is because of the pressure drop across the near-boiler piping and the boiler itself. This is why no hot water from the boiler blends into the return water from the radiant circuit, raising its temperature before it can hit the boiler. A power of "2" can't possibly overcome a power of "7." Low pressure can't go to high pressure. It would be like trying to put 30-psi of air pressure in your car's tires with a compressor that you had set for 20 psi. It just won't work.

And that's why, in a true primary-secondary system with four-way valves, you should get into the habit of using two circulators. Unless, of course, you're not concerned about flue-gas condensation in the boiler.

When you think about it, unless it has both a primary and a secondary circulator, a four-way valve is actually a three-way valve!

Meanwhile, back in the boiler room

Okay, the equations and guidelines we've used so far will go with us as we move into the boiler room. Let's begin by looking at a primary-secondary system that has just one boiler.

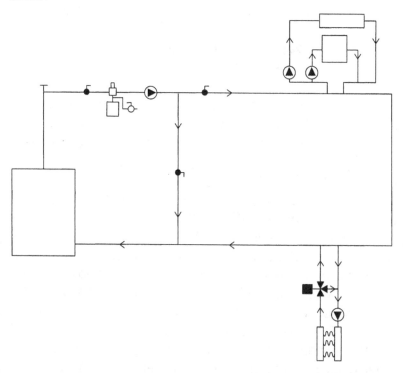

We tapped right into the supply and return of the boiler, just as we would with a hydronic system that didn't involve primary-secondary pumping. I've put a system bypass from the discharge side of the circulator back to the return side of the boiler, though. This is the bypass I've been mention- ing all along. Its job is to take hot water from the boiler's supply side and mix it with the relatively cool water that's returning from the system. We sized our system to ensure that the return water wouldn't drop below 140°F, but the system bypass gives us a margin of safety against flue-gas condensation by raising the temperature of the returning water a bit.

The flow rate across the boiler is easy to figure. Just take the supply temperature and subtract the return temperature. That gives us the ΔT we'll need for the GPM equation. If we're figuring the flow rate and pipe size for the system we've been working with, it would look like this:

$$\frac{245,000 \text{ BTUH}}{40°F \ \Delta T \ X \ 500} = 12.25 \text{ GPM}$$

I'd use 1-1/4" pipe for that as well, even though a boiler of this size will probably have 1-1/2" supply-and-return tappings. You'll need to use a balancing valve in the system bypass line, and another at the circulator's discharge to get the flow rates set up properly. There's a simpler way to do this, though. You can use a thermostatic system bypass valve made by ESBE (and distributed by Danfoss Automatic Controls in the U.S.A.). This valve has three, clearly labeled ports and it contains a thermostat that's similar to the one in your car's radiator. The thermostat keeps the boiler water circulating around the boiler as long as the boiler water temperature is below 160°F. Between 160°F and 170°F, the valve begins to allow some of the water out into the system, while bypassing the rest into the return to meet what's returning from the system. When the boiler reaches 180°F, all the water flows from the boiler to the system. If you get yourself an inexpensive ESBE valve, you'll save yourself the cost of two balancing valves and some fiddling. ESBE makes the operation automatic, and they do a fine job of protecting boilers that can't take low-temperature water.

Okay, let's try something different. Let's split the total load between two boilers.

Here, we're using two boilers, each with a rating of 125,000 BTUH. They're going to take care of the same sys-

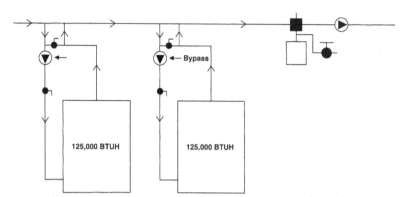

tem we've been looking at all along, and the reason we're using two boilers is because it doesn't get that cold every day. That's one of the advantages of primary-secondary pumping. It gives us a way to shed load on a mild day without having to move water through a boiler that's not running (which wastes energy to standby losses).

We'll size the piping for the boilers the same way we did earlier, but we'll need to adjust the loads because each boiler is smaller.

$$\frac{\textbf{125,000 BTUH}}{\textbf{40°F ΔT X 500}} = \textbf{6.25 GPM}$$

I'd use 1" pipe for that and a small circulator. Here again, use either a system bypass line, or an ESBE valve to further protect the boiler against low-temperature returns.

When we have multiple boilers, we also have an additional circulator. It's the one that's taking care of the primary main. Its job is to shuttle water around, making it available to both the boilers and the secondary circuits. Think of it as a hydronic monorail. The boilers (which are now on secondary circuits) put in the heat, while the radiators (on their own secondary circuits) remove the heat. The primary water (the monorail) is in continuous motion. If it's cold outside, the primary pump will be on. It's as simple as that. We'll start and stop the boilers as needed, and we may or may not do the same with the secondary radiation circuits (depending on whether or not they're operating on outdoor-air reset controls).

Can you see how the boilers will work? The way we have them piped, the primary water will keep passing across the common piping until the boiler's secondary circulator starts. Then, the boiler's circulator will draw water out of the primary, through the boiler, and back into the primary. On a very cold day, the secondary circuits will try to remove more heat from the primary flow than a single boiler can put in, so the second boiler will start and the two will work together to meet the needs of the system.

And the beauty part of this is that no water will flow through a boiler when it's off, and you can easily set the boilers for lead-lag operation, which helps spread out the wear and tear.

The number of boilers you can use in a primary-secondary system depends a lot on the type of boiler you're using. You have to take a close look at the venting needs of the boilers and question what will happen if you're using, say, 10 boilers, and just one is trying to vent into a chimney that's designed for the full-blown load of 10 boilers. With some boilers, this isn't a concern, however, so make this a part of your planning when you're selecting equipment. Every job has its own unique requirements.

Here's another way you can pipe multiple boilers.

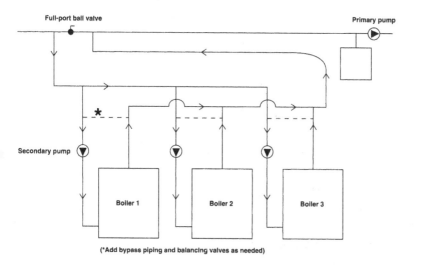

Full-port ball valve

Primary pump

Secondary pump

Boiler 1

Boiler 2

Boiler 3

(*Add bypass piping and balancing valves as needed)

Here, we have them in reverse-return. The first boiler supplied is the last boiler returned. It involves more piping, but it's a better arrangement because each boiler will be seeing the same return temperature (it's a manifold!). That first boiler-room piping arrangement has some disadvantages because, on a cold day when both boilers are running, the second boiler will get return water that has already been through the first boiler. This might cause the second boiler to short-cycle because of the potentially small difference in temperature between its return and its supply.

Notice, too, that with either arrangement we only need one compression tank. It belongs right at the suction side of the primary circulator. If we had just one boiler, the tank would be on the suction side of the primary circulator as well. Here, with two boilers, the compression tank belongs in the primary piping, not on the boilers. The "compression tank" for each boiler will be the common piping that connects it to the primary circuit. Notice how the boiler circulators are pumping away from the common piping. That means they'll add their differential pressure to the static fill pressure in the boiler. As we discussed earlier, the only time you shouldn't pipe your boiler pumps this way is when you're concerned that the additional pump head might pop the relief valve.

When you size a compression tank you have to take into consideration:

1. The volume of water in the system.

2. The average water temperature in the system.

3. The difference in pressure between the fill valve and the relief valve.

4. The fluid that you're circulating (if it's not water).

You take those four things to a compression-tank manufacturer's catalog and select the tank that's right for that system. When you're sizing a tank for a primary-secondary system you have to make sure you measure all the water in all the piping and equipment. You'll be basing the size of the tank on the TOTAL water volume of the system, which brings me to an interesting point. If a primary-secondary system has an undersized compression tank, or if the compression tank has lost some of its air, you may not notice the problem during the fall and the spring. That's because not all of the zones are calling for heat. Some of the system water remains cool and doesn't expand. But in the dead of winter, when most or all of the zones are up and running, the tank that seemed fine before is suddenly undersized and the relief valve is popping. "Undersized" is a relative term. It all depends on the time of year. Stick that in the back of your mind because it can happen on *any* job that has zones.

Next, figure the average water temperature as being the mid-point of the temperature drop across the primary main. So if the water leaves the boiler at 180°F and returns at 140°F, you'd use 160°F as the average water temperature when you're sizing the tank.

The fill pressure is whatever pressure you need to lift water to the top of the system and keep it under 3-psi pressure once it's there. When you're sizing the tank, you take the fill pressure at the point where you're going to install the tank. This is the reason why you'll often see tanks installed in the attic space of some buildings. The higher the tank is in the system, the smaller it can be.

The relief valve setting is whatever the boiler requires. If you had a system with a 12-psi fill pressure (at the tank) and a 30-psi relief pressure, you would use 18 psi as your differential when sizing your compression tank. If you were filling the system at 18-psi pressure and the relief valve were set for 30 psi, you'd use 12 psi as your differential. And know that the smaller that differential number gets, the bigger your compression tank will be. And again, this is why you'll sometimes see tanks in attics. If you put the tank way up there, it's only going to see the pressure that's at the top of the system, which is usually 3 psi. The difference between 3-psi fill pressure and 30-psi relief pressure is what makes for a smaller tank.

Now for the air separator.

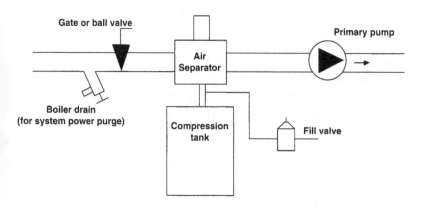

A good place to pipe the air separator is at the suction side of the primary circulator (where the pressure is lowest), and near the boiler (where the water is hottest). If you set-up your system with full-port ball valves in the common piping (on one-pipe systems), or with balancing valves (on two-pipe systems with two-way valves), you'll be able to "power-purge" the initial air out of the system. Catch the air back in the primary circuit, just before the primary pump. All it takes to do this is a ball- or gate-valve and a boiler drain. That will be your single purge point for the entire system. The air separator will take care of the air that will leave the water as the system heats up.

And notice that I've placed the system fill valve in the compression tank's line. This is a point of no pressure change, a place in the system that no circulator can affect. And if you're using that power-purge set-up you'll be able to blast the air right through the system by using the fast-fill feature on your fill valve.

Those are the basic components. I think you should also use a low-water cutoff on each boiler, whether or not the local code requires it. A low-water cutoff can save lives, and the price of this important device disappears in the price of the job. Do yourself and your customers a favor by using low-water cutoffs, *especially* on radiant jobs where some or all of the tubing is below the boiler.

As for controls, we're fortunate to be working during a time when there are a number of terrific manufacturers making electronic controls that can manage all the mechanical components of a primary-secondary system with ease. Once you've decided on how to pipe your system, check with the control manufacturer of your choice as to which of their products best matches your system's needs. They'll take it from there.

"A difference to <u>be</u> a difference has to <u>make</u> a difference."

What Gil Carlson taught me has made a difference in my professional life. He wrote mainly to engineers, which I am not, and I had to work hard to understand the underlying principles that he laid out. I hope I've done a good job explaining what he dreamed up and developed so that you can use this knowledge to make a difference in <u>your</u> life. Gil helped me see the magic. I hope that I've helped you see it as well.

Primary-secondary pumping can make a difference on every job you do, if you take the time to plan ahead. Good planning beats guesswork every time. Good planning helps you avoid oversizing. If you use the simple equations in this book you should be able to reduce the cost of the installation, while meeting your clients' needs on every job.

And as you're piping those jobs, please take a moment to remember the late, great Gil Carlson. He lived a life that was filled with discovery, sharing, and a passion for his chosen profession. Whatever goes into a life, must come out of that life, and a small part of what came out of *his* life is this book. He was my teacher, and I was lucky enough to get to sit at his knee for a while.

Good luck to you. Make a difference.

Made in United States
Troutdale, OR
12/26/2024

27279182R00070